Conquering the AMC 8

JAI SHARMA AND RITHWIK NUKALA

November 10, 2020

This book was formatted using LATEX and Evan Chen's style sheet. Here is the copyright notice:

Special Thanks from Jai

- To my sister, mother, and father for supporting me through the production of the material.

- To Christopher Sun for making the cover page of this book.

- To the students of the 2020 summer AMC 8 Preparation Class for helping me grow as a teacher and learn how to communicate with students.

- To the Art of Problem Solving Website for a full list of AMC 8 problems.

Special Thanks from Rithwik

- To my dad for helping me develop a liking for math.

- To the students of the 2020 summer AMC 8 Preparation Class for helping me to grow as a public speaker and teacher.

Best wishes to the students of this book on the AMC 8 and other math competitions!

Contents

I   Test Taking Strategies for the AMC 8   5

1 Introduction   6

2 How to Practice Effectively   6

3 The Day of the Exam   8

II Number Sense in the AMC 8   9

4 Introduction   10

5 Different Types of Numbers   10

6 Basic Number Sense   11
   6.1 Basic Number Sense Problems 14

7 Percentage and Interest   14
   7.1 Percentage and Interest Problems 19

8 Proportions and Ratios   20
   8.1 Proportions and Ratios Problems 24

9 Simple Statistics   25
   9.1 Simple Statistics Problems 26

10 Averages   27
   10.1 Averages Problems 28

11 Venn Diagrams   29
   11.1 Venn Diagrams Problems 30

12 Conversion Factors   31
   12.1 Conversion Factors Problems 33

13 Magic Grids   33

III Number Theory in the AMC 8   36

14 Introduction   37

15 Modular Arithmetic   37
15.1 Parity 46
15.2 Modular Arithmetic Problems 47

16 Converting Bases   48
16.1 Converting Bases Problems 52

17 Prime Numbers   52
17.1 Prime Number Problems 55

18 GCD   55
18.1 GCD Practice Problems 57

19 LCM   57
19.1 LCM Practice Problems 59

20 Euclidean Algorithm   59
20.1 Euclidean Algorithm Practice Problems 63

IV   Algebra in the AMC 8   64

21 Introduction   65

22 Sequences and Series   65
22.1 Arithmetic Sequences and Series 67
22.2 Geometric Sequences and Series 69
22.3 Sequences and Series Practice Problems 70

23 Introduction to Complex Numbers and the Argand Plane   70
23.1 Introduction to Complex Numbers and the Argand Plane Problems 73

24 Introduction to Functions   74
24.1 Introduction to Functions Practice Problems 75

25 Linear Equations   76
25.1 Linear Equations Practice Problems 77

26 Systems of Equations   77

27 Introduction to Polynomials   79

28 Quadratics   81

29 Vieta's Formulas   85

30 Rationalizing the Denominator   **88**

31 Linear Inequalities   **89**

32 Quadratic inequalities   **90**

33 Graphing Equations and Inequalities   **91**

34 Transforming Graphs   **97**
34.1 Graphing Systems of Equations 103

35 Useful Expansions and Symmetric Sums   **105**

36 Rate Problems and More Proportions   **108**

37 Linear Equation Word Problems   **110**

38 Exponents and Logarithms   **112**

V   Counting and Probability in the AMC 8   **114**

39 Introduction   **115**

40 Basic Counting   **115**
40.1 Basic Counting Problems 119

41 Factorial!   **120**
41.1 Factorial! Problems 122

42 Permutations   **123**
42.1 Permutations Problems 126

43 Combinations   **126**
43.1 Combinations Problems 128

44 Pascal's Triangle   **129**
44.1 Pascal's Triangle Problems 133

45 Binomial Theorem   **134**
45.1 Binomial Theorem Problems 136

46 Introduction to Probability   **136**

47 Multiplying Probabilities   **139**

48 Adding Probabilities   **141**

49 Casework   **143**

50 Complementary Counting   **144**
50.1 Complimentary Counting Problems 146

51 Counting and Probability Problems   **147**

VI   Geometry in the AMC 8   **151**

52 Introduction   **152**

53 Basic Definitions   **152**
53.1 Basic Definitions Problems 158

54 The Pythagorean Theorem   **159**

55 Area of Triangles   **162**

56 Perimeter of Triangles   **165**
56.1 Perimeter of Triangles Problems 167

57 Area of Polygons   **169**
57.1 Area of Quadrilaterals 169
57.2 Area of Squares 170
57.3 Area of Rectangles 172
    57.3.1 Area of Squares and Rectangles Problems 173
57.4 Area of Parallelograms 174
    57.4.1 Area of Parallelograms Problems 176
57.5 Area of Rhombuses 177
    57.5.1 Area of Rhombus Problems 180
57.6 Area of Trapezoids 180
    57.6.1 Area of Trapezoids Problems 183
57.7 General Area of Polygons 184

58 Similar and Congruent Triangles   **186**
58.1 Similar Triangles 186
58.2 Congruent Triangles 196
58.3 Similar and Congruent Triangles Problems 201

59 Circles   **203**
59.1 Circumference 204
59.2 Area 206

59.3 Sectors 209

60 Geometry Problems **211**

VII Advanced Competition Tricks for the AMC 8 **224**

61 Introduction **225**

62 Mental Math and Computation Tricks **225**
    62.1 Summing Large Numbers 225
    62.2 Multiplication Tricks 226
        62.2.1 Multiplication by 10 226
        62.2.2 Multiplication by 5 227
        62.2.3 Multiplication of a Two Digit Number by 11 227
        62.2.4 Two Digit Multiplication Trick 1 228
        62.2.5 Two Digit Multiplication Trick 2 229
    62.3 Squaring Tricks 230
    62.4 Using Difference of Squares for Factorization 231

63 Divisibility Rules **232**

Part I
Test Taking Strategies for the AMC 8

§1 Introduction

The American Mathematics Competition (AMC) series is a group of contests that judge students' mathematical abilities in the form of a timed test. The AMC 8 is the introductory level competition in this series and is taken by tens of thousands of students every year in grades 8 and below. Students are given 40 minutes to complete the 25 question test. Every right answer receives 1 point and there is no penalty for wrong or missing answers, so the maximum possible score is 25/25. While all AMC 8 problems can be solved without any knowledge of trigonometry, calculus, or more advanced high school mathematics, they can be tantalizingly difficult to attempt without much prior experience and can take many years to master because problems often have complex wording and test the knowledge of mathematical concepts that are not covered in the school curriculum.

This book is meant to teach the skills necessary to solve mostly any problem on the AMC 8. However, our goal is to not only teach you how to perfect the AMC 8, but we also want you to learn and understand the topics presented as if you were in a classroom setting. Above all, the first and foremost goal is for you to have a good time learning math!

§2 How to Practice Effectively

There are around 20 past tests for the AMC 8. Using this limited set of practice, how are you supposed to practice effectively to ensure the highest score possible on the AMC 8? We have compiled the most helpful strategies for preparing below:

- **Answer every question!** Because there is no penalty for a wrong answer, make sure that you answer every question even if you are not sure of the answer. Even if you guess, there is a chance that you are right!

- **Mark problems that you find hard.** Even if you are able to solve a problem **and** get the right answer, it does not hurt to mark a question with an arrow if you found it unusually challenging. After you finish the practice test, go back and review the solution to that problem. Almost all of the time, there is a better, more efficient way to solve the same problem!

- **Review all incorrect problems.** This should be obvious, but it is also one of the most important tactics on this list. You should also sort your mistakes into categories. For example, if you get a Number Theory problem wrong, make a note of what Number Theory topic you must study again. If the mistake is not conceptual and rather just an arithmetic mistake, make a note of this.

- **Make a list of problems that you get wrong, problems you are not able to solve, or problems where you do not use the most efficient solution the**

first time. A few weeks before the AMC 8 exam, look back on this list and solve the problems again and see if you solve the problem with the best solution. If not, then repeat!

- **Practice with less time.** In the AMC 8 exam, time is of the essence! Even if you are able to attempt all problems of an exam in only 40 minutes or even 35 minutes, you will always take more time on the real test. In order to combat this, attempt your first test and record how long it takes you to attempt all the problems to the best of your ability. Preferably, this should be no more than 50 minutes to 1 hour (after learning the material in the book, it will be much less). Then, give yourself 5 less minutes for the next test, and 10 minutes less for the test after that. Slowly, you will decrease the amount of time that it take you to complete the test. Keep on going, adjusting the rate at which you decrease your time according to your comfort level until you reach 25 to 30 minutes. If you can keep going, even better, but this range is a very good level for the AMC 8.

- **Practice, Practice, PRACTICE!** This may seem obvious, but you should do all of the practice tests available on the Art of Problem Solving Website. It would be wise to also record your scores (see next point) as you go along. Ideally, you should do every test at least 2-3 times. Depending on how much time you have before the actual test, you should prioritize reattempting exams on which you got a lower score. The more practice you have, the better you become accustomed to the problem patterns of the AMC 8.

- **Check your answers.** Not to sound like a broken record, but checking helps to avoid silly mistakes such as arithmetic errors. Checking should not be a matter of if, but when. When doing practice tests, spend time to check your answers in the last 5 minutes.

- **Do not be afraid to guess!** If a problem looks too daunting, take your best guess and move on. As I mentioned, time is of the essence! Do not spend 10 minutes on 1 problem because all problems are graded equally. When you finish attempting all the problems, you can come back and spend more time on one that you find tricky. Additionally, there is no penalty for guessing.

- **Record your Scores** After doing each practice test, record your score for that exam. If you know how to use Microsoft Excel or Google Sheets, you should definitely record your scores there. The advantage of using such software tools are that you can plot your scores to see your improvement and you can calculate your average scores very easily. This will also help you to revisit tests on which you do poorly.

Implementing these strategies themselves and practicing will get you very far. However, you must first learn the concepts on the test before or while you attempt a series of practice tests.

§3 The Day of the Exam

While we have mentioned what needs to be done in preparation for the exam, a special address must go to the day of the exam and the day prior to the exam. Here are some things that you should do:

- **Do not do last minute studying!** Last minute studying never helps, regardless of whether you are taking the AMC 8. Do not study math on the day before the exam. You have worked so hard, and now it is time to relax! Furthermore, you seldom retain information from last minute studying. On the contrary, studying on the day before can even hurt your score.

- **Sleep early.** A good night's rest is crucial in determining your performance in the AMC 8 test. Sleeping early will also help to avoid any last minute stress that you may have.

- **Eat a good breakfast.** Similar to sleeping, this will help to boost your mental abilities and therefore your test score.

- **Arrive early.** Arriving early is better than arriving late. It allows you to face any last minute stress and sort out which pens and pencils you will use. Trivial things like these surprisingly heavily influence your test results.

- **Mark questions you are unsure of.** This will ensure that you can easily come back and check your answers.

- **Finish with time to spare.** By this time, you should have mastered completing the test and checking your answers well below the given time limit. Use this to your advantage! Aim to finish the test in around 25 to 30 minutes, so that you have time to redo any questions you skipped or were unsure of.

Part II
Number Sense in the AMC 8

§4 Introduction

This Number Sense handout is our compiled list on how to solve all of the "easy" problems on the AMC 8. This would be around all of the problems between 1 and 10 on a typical AMC 8 test. Most of these problems require simple logic and computation, but we mention it here as a way of introducing you to the different types of problems you will encounter on the AMC 8. Some of the practice problems are meant to be challenging. This is why a hint could be given along with the problem statement. The answer to all of the competition practice problems can be found online by using their respective problem numbers.

§5 Different Types of Numbers

There are many different groups of numbers in mathematics. The overarching umbrella term for all known numbers is referred to as complex numbers. Complex numbers include real and imaginary parts. We will be looking at imaginary numbers much later, but for now, we focus on the real numbers.

Real numbers are divided into three large categories: positives, negatives, and zero. The last group, as you may have guessed, comprises of only one number: 0. We can "plot" the real numbers on a tool called the number line. The number line is a line that spans left and right forever and we usually denote that they are endless by writing arrows on either side of the part of the number line we wish to view. In the middle of the number line, we find the number 0. On the right of zero are all of the positive numbers, which can be divided further into more categories, as we will see shortly. Similarly, on the left hand side of 0 lie all of the negative numbers. To denote a number as negative, we write the number's positive counterpart with a "-" in front of it. For example, the number "negative five" can be expressed simply as -5.

As I mentioned, the real numbers can be categorized further. If a number has no fractional or decimal part, it is called an integer. The numbers

$$-2048, 0, \text{ and } 5$$

are examples of integers, while

$$-15.45, 0.001, 3.14, \text{ and } 12\frac{345}{678}$$

are not. Whole numbers are the set

$$0, 1, 2, 3, 4, \cdots$$

Natural numbers, or counting numbers, are what they sound like:

$$1, 2, 3, 4, 5, \cdots$$

However, there are also numbers that are not integers. For example, rational numbers are numbers that can be expressed as the ratio, or fraction, of two integers. For example,

$$-\frac{4}{1}, \frac{0}{1}, \frac{2334}{4332}, 0.1 = \frac{1}{10}$$

are all examples of rational numbers, while

$$\sqrt{2} \approx 1.414, \pi \approx 3.14159, \text{ and } e \approx 2.71828$$

are not. Real numbers that are not rational are called irrational. Three examples are shown above. All integers are rational numbers. Interesting things happen when we take the square root, cube root, or the nth root of integers. When we take a square root of a number, or the second root of a number, we find a number, when multiplied by itself, gives the number that we started with. For example $\sqrt{4} = 2$ because $2 \cdot 2 = 2^2 = 4$. Similary, when we find the cube root of a number, or the third root of a number, we find a number, when multiplied by itself thrice gives the number we started with. For example $\sqrt[3]{27} = 3$ because $3 \cdot 3 \cdot 3 = 3^3 = 27$. Similarly, taking the nth root of a number means to find a number, when multiplied by itself n times, or when raised to the power n results in the number that we started with. Many times, when we take the nth root of a number (where n is an integer greater than 1), we get an irrational number. These numbers are called radicals. There are more categorizations, but this is mostly all you will need to know for the AMC 8.

§6 Basic Number Sense

Basic number sense entails all problems that can be solved with simple computation or logic. Not much skill is required for these problems. This specific section addresses the problems 1-5 on a typical AMC 8 test. For example:

> **Problem 1** (Problem 3: AMC 8 2000)
> How many whole numbers lie in the interval between $\frac{5}{3}$ and 2π?

Proof. Notice how the problem says whole numbers. As we just learned, whole numbers are numbers like $1, 2, 3, \cdots$. By simple observation, we know that $\frac{5}{3}$ is between 1 and 2. Additionally, π can be approximated as 3.14, so 2π is about 6.28, which is between 6 and 7. Therefore, the whole numbers in this interval, or the whole numbers between $\frac{5}{3}$ and 2π, are 2, 3, 4, 5, and 6. Therefore, the number of whole numbers in the given "interval" is $\boxed{5}$. □

15

If you knew the approximate values of $\frac{5}{3}$ and 2π, then the problem required little to no skill. However, do not overlook these problems. You may view these problems as free points that can easily boost your score, so make sure you get them right! Let's look at a few more types of problems like this:

> **Problem 2** (Problem 1: AMC 8 2000)
>
> Aunt Anna is 42 years old. Caitlin is 5 years younger than Brianna, and Brianna is half as old as Aunt Anna. How old is Caitlin?

Proof. This is just a computation problem with a little bit of tricky wording. We are given that Aunt Anna is 42 year old, but the rest of the information is presented in reverse. Specifically, we cannot use the knowledge that Caitlin is 5 years younger than Brianna without knowing either Caitlin or Brianna's age. This is why we must use the information that Brianna is half as old as Aunt Anna; we already know Aunt Anna's age, so we can find Brianna's age because she is half as old. Then, Brianna's age is $\frac{42}{2} = 21$. **Now** we can use the information that Caitlin is 5 years younger than Brianna. Hence, since Brianna is 21 years old, Caitlin must be 5 years younger, or $21 - 5 = \boxed{16}$ years old. $\qquad\square$

> **Remark 6.1.** AMC 8 problems are known for their twisty wording and test makers know this! Don't fall into this trap! Instead, it is often helpful to take a step back and find out what the problem means without all of the complex numbers. In this case, the problem was relating the ages of a few friends and asking the test taker to compute the age of one of the friends with the given information.

> **Problem 3** (Problem 4: AMC 8 2007)
>
> A haunted house has six windows. In how many ways can Georgie the Ghost enter the house by one window and leave by a different window?

Proof. While this problem can be solved using counting techniques and complicated formulas, it is best solved in the most intuitive way. Think about this problem for a minute from the point of view of Georgie the Ghost (this is the logic and intuition I was referring to earlier). Georgie can enter the house through any one of the six windows. Now, once he is in the house, he can exit the house through any of the other five windows. So, for every one of the six windows that he goes into, there are five windows through which he can come out. Naively, one could count the routes as follows:

- if Georgie goes through the first window, there are 5 windows he can go through;

- alternatively, if he goes through the second window, there are 5 windows he can go through;

16

- alternatively, if he goes through the third window, there are 5 windows he can go through...

We can continue like this until we reach the sixth window, but we have a simple tool that allows us to add the same thing over and over: multiplication! We are counting 5 different paths for every window, and there are 6 windows. Therefore, we are computing $5 + 5 + 5 + 5 + 5 + 5 = 5 \cdot 6 = \boxed{30}$ ways. $\qquad \square$

This last problem was not too hard after we broke the problem down and viewed the problem in cases. This is a powerful problem solving tool.

> **Remark 6.2.** If a problem seems confusing because there is just too much going on, try breaking the problem down into cases.

Let's keep going.

> **Problem 4** (Problem 1: AMC 8 2010)
> At Euclid Middle School, the mathematics teachers are Miss Germain, Mr. Newton, and Mrs. Young. There are 11 students in Mrs. Germain's class, 8 students in Mr. Newton's class, and 9 students in Mrs. Young's class taking the AMC 8 this year. How many mathematics students at Euclid Middle School are taking the contest?

Proof. If you do not already see the simplicity of this problem, we are just asked to add the number of students taking the AMC 8 from each class. So, we get $11 + 8 + 9 = \boxed{28}$ students at Euclid Middle School taking the AMC 8. $\qquad \square$

One more...

> **Problem 5** (Problem 3: AMC 8 2008)
> If February is a month that contains Friday the 13th, what day of the week is February 1?

Proof. Again, we think about this logically - that is basically all you have to do for the first five problems. The day February 1 occurs exactly 12 days before February 13. Since a week contains seven days, 12 days is 2 days short of 2 weeks. For obvious reasons, any two days that are a whole number of weeks apart occur on the same day of the week. For example, if today is Friday, it will be Friday again one week from now, and again one week after that. Therefore, if February 13 occurs on Friday, the day two weeks before February 13, or January 30, will occur on Friday as well. Oops! This is not the answer, though! What happened? When rewinding, we overshot the desired date by 2 days. Therefore, February 1 occurs 2 days after January 30, which is a Friday. So, February 1 occurs on $\boxed{Sunday}$. $\qquad \square$

Remark 6.3. Do not get so lost in the problem that you lose mind of the bigger picture! In this last problem, we got so consumed when focusing on rewinding the date by 2 weeks that we forgot to add the 2 days we overshot by.

By now, you should get a feel for the types of problems that occur in the 1-5 problem range. Most of the time, these problems are (as mentioned before) free points. But do not rush through them and get an easy problem wrong for a careless mistake! These problems are where you collect your free points and they can easily put you above the majority of the competition.

§6.1 Basic Number Sense Problems

Problem 6 (Problem 1: AMC 8 2005)

Connie multiplies a number by 2 and gets 60 as her answer. However, she should have divided the number by 2 to get the correct answer. What is the correct answer?

Problem 7 (Problem 5: AMC 8 2005)

Soda is sold in packs of 6, 12 and 24 cans. What is the minimum number of packs needed to buy exactly 90 cans of soda?

Problem 8

Big Al the ape ate 100 delicious yellow bananas from May 1 through May 5. Each day he ate six more bananas than on the previous day. How many delicious bananas did Big Al eat on May 5? (Hint: Try to substitute a variable for the number of bananas eaten on May 1.)

§7 Percentage and Interest

Percentage is a topic that frequently occurs on the AMC 8. First, we will start with a definition:

Definition 7.1 (Percentage) — Percentage is the number of parts per 100. Specifically, if I divide a number (or an object) into 100 parts, the percentage will tell us how many of those parts we are referring to.

Let's try a concrete example.

Problem 9

What is 5% of 200?

Proof. First, we must divide 200 into 100 parts. Each part will have a size of $\frac{200}{100} = 2$. Since we are taking 5% of 200, we are referring to 5 of these small parts. Therefore, 5 parts will have a size of $5 \cdot 2 = 10$. Therefore, 5% of 200 is $\boxed{10}$. $\square$

You might have seen that instead of making this solution very long, we could have avoided much of the intuition we provided by simply:

- Dividing the number by 100;

- Multiplying this result by the percentage we want.

This is how we will normally determine percentages when we are asked to compute them. If we want to find $p\%$ of a number n, we compute

$$n \cdot \frac{p}{100} = \frac{n \cdot p}{100}.$$

It turns out that p in the above formula can be larger than 100.

Problem 10

What is 500% of 50?

Proof. By the above formula, we can compute the answer to be $50 \cdot \frac{500}{100} = 50 \cdot 5 = \boxed{250}$. $\square$

Another way of viewing this is that when we take $p\%$ of a number n, we are "shifting" the decimal point of p two spaces to the left before multiplying this result by n. Note that this is the same as dividing by 100. To illustrate, when we divided 500 by 100 in the last example, we "shifted" the decimal two spaces to the right to get 5. Similarly, if we divide 60 by 100, we "shift" the decimal 2 spaces to the left to get 0.6. (Remember, in a whole number, the decimal point is to the rightmost of the number. So, $60 = 60.0$, and shifting the decimal gives us our answer we just got.) Let us try a different type of example:

Problem 11

What percent of 30 is 5?

Proof. Let p be our answer so that $\frac{30 \cdot p}{100} = 5$. Then, $p = \frac{5 \cdot 100}{30} = \boxed{\frac{50}{3}}$. Since $\frac{50}{3} \approx 16.6$, we can also say that $\boxed{16.6\%}$ of 30 is 5. $\square$

Let us make this more general. Let us try to find:

Problem 12

What percent of a number m is n?

Proof. Again, suppose that p is our answer so that $\frac{m \cdot p}{100} = n$. Then, solving for p, we get $p = \frac{n \cdot 100}{m}$. $\qquad\square$

So, this is the general form if we are asked this type of question.

Now, let us try some competition problems:

Problem 13 (Problem 9: AMC 8 2010)

Ryan got 80% of the problems correct on a 25-problem test, 90% on a 40-problem test, and 70% on a 10-problem test. What percent of all the problems did Ryan answer correctly?

Proof. First, we find the number of problems he solved correctly on the first test. This is $80\% of 25$, or $25 \cdot 0.8 = 20$. Similarly, the number of correct problems on the second test is $40 \cdot 0.9 = 36$ and the number of correct problems on the third test is $10 \cdot 0.7 = 7$. Adding these three results, we get $20 + 36 + 7 = 63$ total correct problems. However, the problem is asking us for the **percent** of correct problems, not the total correct problems. Make sure you see the difference!

> **Remark 7.2.** Focus on what the problem is asking! Do not get so carried away when doing computation that you forget the objective of the problem.

We get the total number of problems across the three tests to be $25 + 40 + 10 = 75$ total problems. Therefore (from our previous example), the percent of correct problems is $\frac{63 \cdot 100}{75} = \boxed{84\%}$. $\qquad\square$

This problem actually illustrates both of the formulas that we just learned. Specifically, we used the first formula when computing the number of correct problems on each respective test, and we used the second formula when computing the percent of correct problems. Let us move onto something a bit more advanced: investing money into banks. When you invest money into banks, banks give you bits of money for the time that you keep the money with them, called interest. We start with a definition to calculate the interest for a general investment:

> **Definition 7.3** (Simple Interest) — **Simple interest** is defined as follows: If I invest $\$p$ in a bank that gives simple interest at an **interest rate** of r, in t years, I will have gained, in interest, $\$(p \cdot r \cdot t)$. If i is my interest, then $i = p \cdot r \cdot t$.

This should intuitively make sense. If I invest p dollars, I should be given returns based on the interest rate as well as the amount of time that I invest in the given bank. This type of problem does not occur often on the AMC 8, so two examples should suffice:

Problem 14

If I invest $500 at an interest rate of 5% for 10 years in a simple interest bank, how much interest will I have generated? How much total money will I have?

Proof. By our formula, I will have generated

$$i = 500 \cdot 5\% \cdot 10 = 500 \cdot 0.05 \cdot 10 = \boxed{\$250}.$$

Notice how we substituted 0.05 for 5%. But what is our total amount of money? We generated $250 in interest, but that is less than we originally started with. This cannot possibly be the total amount of money. That is because it is not. Going back to our definition for simple interest, we see that we simply generated $250 more than our original 500. This becomes $500 + 250 = \boxed{750}$. $\square$

Let us try the same kind of problem in a reverse direction:

Problem 15

I invest $1000 into a simple interest bank at a rate of 10%. How long should I leave the money in the bank in order to generate $3000 in total?

Note that the interest rate used in this problem is very unrealistic and is only chosen as an example.

Proof. The $3000 includes the initial $1000, so I generated $3000 - \$1000 = \$2000$ in interest. We substitute the known values into the formula $i = p \cdot r \cdot t$. We do not know t, but we know the rest. Hence, $i = 2000$, $r = 10\% = 0.1$, and $p = 1000$ (p is the amount that we initially invested). So, $2000 = 1000 \cdot 0.1 \cdot t$. Solving for t, we get $t = \frac{2000}{1000 \cdot 0.1} = \boxed{20 \text{years}}$. $\square$

Now that we have learned about simple interest, it might be disheartening to hear that almost no bank in the world uses simple interest in real life. Instead, they use something called Compound Interest:

21

Definition 7.4 (Compound Interest) — **Compound interest** is defined as follows: If I invest \$$p$ in a bank that gives compound interest at an interest rate of r, in t years, I will have (in total) $p \cdot \left(1 + \frac{r}{100}\right)^t$ dollars.

This definition is very technical, but what does it really mean? Fundamentally, compound interest can be explained as follows:

Example 7.5

Let us invest \$100 into a compound interest bank at 5% interest rate. Using compound interest, our interest gained by the end of the first year is $100 \cdot 5\% = 100 \cdot 0.05$. Adding this to the original \$100 we invested, we get our total balance to be $100 + 100 \cdot 0.05 = (100 \cdot 1) + (100 \cdot 0.05)$, which we can factor as

$$100(1 + 0.05) = 100(1.05).$$

We will not calculate this out by hand just yet. Notice how the balance is equivalent to the original amount we invested multiplied by 1 more than the interest rate. This is because we are adding the original to the interest we generate. Now, we focus on the balance at the end of two years. Investing our money once again into this bank, we find that we will generate an interest of $(100 \cdot 1.05) \cdot 0.05$. This means that the total balance at the end of two years will be the amount at the start of the year plus this interest. This is $(100 \cdot 1.05) + (100 \cdot 1.05) \cdot 0.05 = (100 \cdot 1.05) \cdot 1 + (100 \cdot 1.05) \cdot 0.05$. We can factor this as

$$(100 \cdot 1.05) \cdot (1 + 0.05) = (100 \cdot 1.05) \cdot 1.05.$$

Wow! We find the same constant 1.05 again! Thinking about this, we find that every year, if we invest \$$p$, then we will gain $p \cdot 0.05$ dollars in interest. Adding this to p, we get $p + p \cdot 0.05 = p \cdot 1 + p \cdot 0.05$. Again, this can be factored as

$$p \cdot (1 + 0.05) = p \cdot (1.05).$$

Therefore, if we have $(100 \cdot 1.05) \cdot 1.05$ dollars at the end of 2 years as we just found, we will have $((100 \cdot 1.05) \cdot 1.05) \cdot 1.05$. We can generalize this by noting that at the end of each year, our money is multiplied by 1.05. Through simple observation, we find that after t years, we will have $100 \cdot 1.05^t$ dollars in our account.

Remark 7.6. In the previous example, we assumed that the interest was **compounded** every year. Specifically, we gain 5% interest at the end of each year we invest our money. However, this is not always the case. Interest can be compounded biannually (two times a year), monthly, or even continuously! You will learn about these types of interest in high school, but for the AMC 8, you only need to know about yearly compounding.

Since interest does no appear very frequently on the AMC 8, this is mostly all you need to know!

§7.1 Percentage and Interest Problems

Problem 16 (Problem 2: AMC 8 2005)

Karl bought five folders from Pay-A-Lot at a cost of \$2.50 each. Pay-A-Lot had a 20%-off sale the following day. How much could Karl have saved on the purchase by waiting a day?

Problem 17 (Problem 11: AMC 8 2005)

The sales tax rate in Bergville is 6%. During a sale at the Bergville Coat Closet, the price of a coat is discounted 20% from its \$90.00 price. Two clerks, Jack and Jill, calculate the bill independently. Jack brings up \$90.00 and adds 6% sales tax, then subtracts 20% from this total. Jill rings up \$90.00, subtracts 20% of the price, then adds 6% of the discounted price for sales tax. What is Jack's total minus Jill's total?

Problem 18 (Problem 3: AMC 8 2010)

The graph shows the price of five gallons of gasoline during the first ten months of the year. By what percent is the highest price more than the lowest price?

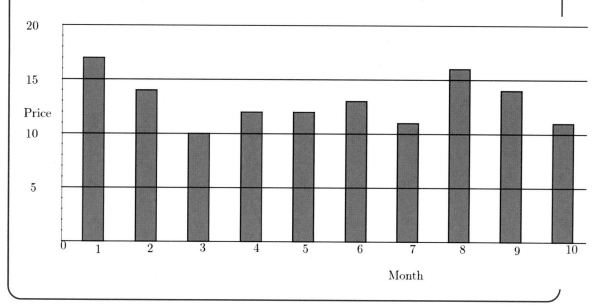

Problem 19 (Problem 15: AMC 2010)

A jar contains 5 different colors of gumdrops. 30% are blue, 20% are brown, 15% are red, 10% are yellow, and other 30 gumdrops are green. If half of the blue gumdrops are replaced with brown gumdrops, how many gumdrops will be brown? (Hint: First, find the **percentage** of brown gumdrops after this replacement.)

Problem 20 (Problem 12: AMC 2010)

Of the 500 balls in a large bag, 80% are red and the rest are blue. How many of the red balls must be removed from the bag so that 75% of the remaining balls are red? (Hint: Set the number of red balls to a certain variable and study how the percentage of red balls change as red balls are removed from the bag.)

Problem 21 (Problem 13: AMC 8 2010)

The lengths of the sides of a triangle in inches are three consecutive integers. The length of the shortest side is 30% of the perimeter. What is the length of the longest side? (Hint: A triangle is a polygon, or a closed shape with straight sides, with 3 sides. The perimeter of a triangle is the sum of the 3 side lengths of the triangle.)

§8 Proportions and Ratios

As we briefly mentioned before, a ratio is like a fraction. In general, a ratio shows the relationship of two different entities. This will become less abstract with an example:

Problem 22

I have a bowl that contains 10 pears and 5 oranges. What is the **ratio of pears to oranges?**

Proof. We can find the ratio of pears to oranges by dividing 10 by 5 to get $\frac{10}{5} = \frac{2}{1}$. But what does this mean? Concretely, the ratio between pears and oranges measures how frequently one fruit occurs in comparison to the other. In this case, since the ratio is $\frac{2}{1}$, we know that for every 2 pears, there is one orange in the bowl. Now the definition at the start of the section makes more sense! In this case, the two entities are pears and oranges. By finding the ratio between these two, we established the said connection. Ratios can also be written as a colon. So, the ratio $\frac{10}{5}$ is the same as $10 : 5$ and $\frac{2}{1}$ can be written as $2 : 1$. As you can see, a ratio sometimes shows the relative frequency between two sets of objects. □

Sometimes, we can go in the reverse direction, deriving conclusions given a ratio between two "entities."

Problem 23

The ratio of apples to pears in a certain colossal bowl is 5:3. If there are 1200 apples, how many pears are there?

Proof. We know that the ratio of apples to pears is 5:3. This means that $\frac{\text{number of apples}}{\text{number of pears}} = \frac{5}{3}$. Substituting what we know, we have $\frac{1200}{\text{number of pears}} = \frac{5}{3}$. A little bit of equation manipulation leads us to find that number of pears $= \frac{1200 \cdot 3}{5} = 720$. So, there are $\boxed{720 \text{ pears}}$ in the gigantic bowl! $\square$

This kind of ratio is called a **direct proportion**. A direct proportion occurs when the quotient of the two entities is a constant. In other words, the ratio of the two entities is constant, as we saw in the last example. By the way, a ratio is not limited to two entities. It can have any number of entities. For example, in the last problem, we could have said that the ratio of apples to pears to oranges was 5:3:2. This means that for every 5 apples, there are 3 pears and 2 oranges. If instead of being asked to find the number of pears we were asked to find the number of oranges, we would have computed that the ratio of apples to oranges was 5:2, so $\frac{\text{number of apples}}{\text{number of oranges}} = \frac{5}{2}$. With the given information, we would make the substitution for the number of apples and found $\frac{1200}{\text{number of oranges}} = \frac{5}{2}$. Manipulating this, we find that number of oranges $= \frac{1200 \cdot 2}{5} = 480$. So, we would have found that there were $\boxed{480 \text{ oranges}}$ in the basket. While we can use more than 2 items in a ratio, we will mostly reduce our computation down to the ratio of two entities, as we just did with apples and pears. Now that we have familiarized ourselves with direct proportions, where the quotient of the entities is constant, we move onto **inverse proportions**. Inverse proportions occur when the **product** of the two entities is constant. Similar to direct proportions, direct proportions can have more than two "entities." Let us first focus on two "entities":

Problem 24

The formula for speed, which we will later learn in detail, is $d = r \cdot t$, where d is the distance traveled, r is the rate, or speed, and t is the amount of time traveled at the given rate.

I am riding my bike. I do not have a speedometer, but I do have a timer. I am riding down a 100 meter hill, and it takes me exactly 20 seconds to ride down the hill. How fast was I going, in meters per second?

Proof. Plugging in the given values into the "speed formula," we find 100 meters $= r \cdot$ 20 seconds. We are trying to find r, or the speed at which I was riding my bike. So, we

25

simply solve for r. We get $r = \frac{100 \text{ meters}}{20 \text{ seconds}} = \boxed{5\dfrac{\text{meters}}{\text{second}}}$. $\qquad\square$

Later, we will learn a bit about the units used in this problem too. In the last two examples, we saw how easy proportion values can be. With some practice, you can learn to identify whether a problem uses ratios or proportions. As you will find, proportion problems can become a little bit tricky because of the wording. Let us try a challenging problem:

Problem 25 (The Art of Problem Solving)

x is directly proportional to the sum of the squares of y and z and inversely proportional to y and the square of z. If $x = 8$ when $y = \frac{1}{2}$ and $z = \frac{\sqrt{3}}{2}$, find y when $x = 1$ and $z = 6$, what is y?

Proof. It would be really nice if we could express the three variables in some sort of way so that they equal a constant.

> **Remark 8.1.** Always look out for opportunities! Wishful thinking goes a long way.

From the given information, we know that x is directly proportional to

$$y^2 + z^2$$

while simultaneously being inversely proportional to

$$y \text{ and } z^2.$$

Extending the logic behind direct proportionality and inverse proportionality, we find that

$$\frac{x \cdot y \cdot z^2}{y^2 + z^2} \tag{*}$$

is constant. We did it! Now, all we need to do is substitute the first set of given values to find that

$$\frac{8 \cdot \frac{1}{2} \cdot \left(\frac{\sqrt{3}}{2}\right)^2}{\left(\frac{1}{2}\right)^2 + \left(\frac{\sqrt{3}}{2}\right)^2} = 3$$

is constant. Then, when $x = 1$ and $z = 6$, our formula (*) above gives

$$\frac{1 \cdot y \cdot 6^2}{y^2 + 6^2} = 3.$$

Simplifying, we get

$$36y = 3y^2 + 3 \cdot 6^2 = 3y^2 + 108.$$

This becomes the quadratic
$$3y^2 - 36y + 108 = 0.$$

Using the quadratic formula, which we will later learn, we find that
$$y = \frac{36 \pm \sqrt{(-36)^2 - 4(3)(108)}}{2(3)} = \frac{36 \pm 0}{6} = \boxed{6}.$$

$\square$

Proportions are extremely applicable, as we will later see in Geometry. For now, we try a simple geometry problem:

Problem 26

In a certain light setting, the length of shadows are directly proportional to the length of the objects that cast them.

A short pole of length 2 meters casts a shadow of length 5 meters. There is a tall 10 meter pole next to it. What is the length of the shadow cast by this pole?

Proof. We know that the length of the two poles are directly proportional to the length of their respective shadows. So, we know that

$$\frac{\text{length of pole}}{\text{length of shadow}}$$

is constant. But what is this constant? Well, we are given both of these values for the smaller pole, so we find the constant to be

$$\frac{\text{length of small pole}}{\text{length of its shadow}} = \frac{2}{5}.$$

We know that this is the same as the ratio between the length of the larger pole and the length of its shadow. So

$$\frac{\text{length of larger pole}}{\text{length of its shadow}} = \frac{10 \text{ meters}}{\text{length of its shadow}} = \frac{2}{5}.$$

Solving for the length of the shadow, which we will call x, we get

$$x = \frac{5}{2} \cdot 10 \text{ meters} = \boxed{25 \text{ meters}}.$$

$\square$

This problem was a case of simple Geometry. We will learn more applications of ratios to Geometry in the Geometry unit.

§8.1 Proportions and Ratios Problems

Problem 27 (Problem 11: AMC 8 2010)

The top of one tree is 16 feet higher than the top of another tree. The heights of the two trees are in the ratio $3:4$. In feet, how tall is the taller tree? (Hint: Try substituting a variable for the length of the shorter tree.)

Problem 28

In a room, 2/5 of the people are wearing gloves, and 3/4 of the people are wearing hats. What is the minimum number of people in the room wearing both a hat and a glove? (Hint: $2/5 + 3/4 > 1$. In other words, the portion of people wearing gloves and wearing hats added together is more than the number of people in the room. By how much, though?)

Problem 29

Hui is an avid reader. She bought a copy of the best seller Math is Beautiful. On the first day, Hui read 1/5 of the pages plus 12 more, and on the second day she read 1/4 of the remaining pages plus 15 pages. On the third day she read 1/3 of the remaining pages plus 18 pages. She then realized that there were only 62 pages left to read, which she read the next day. How many pages are in this book? (Hint: Set the number of pages in the book to a variable. Additionally, note that many proportion problems are also percentage problems. This is because they are almost the same thing.)

Problem 30

A company sells detergent in three different sized boxes: small (S), medium (M) and large (L). The medium size costs 50% more than the small size and contains 20% less detergent than the large size. The large size contains twice as much detergent as the small size and costs 30% more than the medium size. Rank the three sizes from best to worst buy. (Hint: You must use both ratios and percentages here. The "value" of a buy is determined through computing the ratio between the amount of detergent you get to the price you must pay for it. The "best value" is determined by finding which sale yields the greatest value.)

§9 Simple Statistics

In short, simple statistics is comprised of about mean, median and mode. Let's start with a few definitions:

Definition 9.1 — The **mean** of a group of numbers can be found by adding all terms in the set and dividing it by the number of terms. Specifically, the mean can be defined as $\frac{a_1+a_2+a_3+\cdots+a_n}{n}$, where a_1 is the value of the first term, a_2 is the value of the second term, a_3 is the value of the third term, and so on. Additionally, n is the number of terms.

Definition 9.2 — The **median** is the middle most number when all of the numbers of a set are listed from least to greatest (Note: The median of a set cannot be found without ordering the set from least to greatest). For example, say we have an ordered list a_1, a_2, a_3. In this set, a_2 is the middle most number, making it the median. When there is no one number in the middle, we say that the median is the average (or mean) of the middle two numbers.

Definition 9.3 — Finally, the **mode** is the number which occurs most frequently in a set. For example, if our set is 1, 2, 2, the mode would be 2 because it occurs the most frequently.

Another less commonly used statistic on the AMC 8 is:

Definition 9.4 — The **range** of a set is the difference between the maximum and the minimum of a set of numbers. For example, if our set is 1, 2, 5, the range would be 5-1=4.

Problem 31

Consider the set of numbers

$$1, 2, 2, 3, 4, 5, 5, 5, 7, 10, 11, 15.$$

Find the mean, median, and mode of this set.

Proof. In this set, the mean is the sum of all the terms divided by the number of terms. So the mean would be $\frac{1+2+2+3+4+5+5+5+7+10+11+15}{12}$ or $\boxed{\dfrac{31}{6}}$.

The median would be the middle most term with all of the numbers in order. Because this set is already in order and because there are an even number of terms, there will be two numbers in the middle. These numbers are 5 and 5. Taking the average of these two, we get $\frac{5+5}{2} = \boxed{5}$.

The mode of this set is the term which appears the most frequently, or $\boxed{5}$, as it appears 3 times. Note that such sets will almost never be presented in order in problems.

If you are to find the median, you must order the data first before solving. $\square$

Problem 32

What is the mean, median, and mode of the numbers: 2, 0, 1, 3, 0, 3, 3, 1, 2?

Proof. In this set, the mean would be the sum of all the numbers in the set. So the mean would be $\frac{2+0+1+3+0+3+3+1+2}{9}$. This number simplified would be $\boxed{\frac{5}{3}}$.

For the median, because the set is not ordered, we have to order it. The ordered set would be 0, 0, 1, 1, 2, 2, 3, 3, 3. In this ordered set, the middle most number would be 2. So the median of this set is $\boxed{2}$.

The mode is the number which occurs the most often. In this set, the number that occurs the most would be 3, which appears 3 times. So the mode of this set would be $\boxed{3}$. $\square$

§9.1 Simple Statistics Problems

Problem 33 (Problem 4: AMC 8 2010)

What is the sum of the mean, median, and mode of the numbers $2, 3, 0, 3, 1, 4, 0, 3$?

Problem 34 (Problem 5: AMC 8 2015)

Billy's basketball team scored the following points over the course of the first 11 games of the season:

$$42, 47, 53, 53, 58, 58, 58, 61, 64, 65, 73$$

If his team scores 40 in the 12th game, which of the following statistics will show an increase?

(A) range (B) median (C) mean (D) mode (E) mid-range

Problem 35 (Problem 13: AMC 8 2015)

How many subsets of two elements can be removed from the set $\{1, 2, 3, 4, 5, 6, 7, 8, 9, 10, 11\}$ so that the mean (average) of the remaining numbers is 6? (Hint: What is the mean right now? Based on this, by how much must the sum be reduced or increased so that the sum reaches the optimal value? After removing two numbers from this set, how many will remain? How can these last two answers be used to calculate the new mean?)

§10 Averages

An average is the sum of the terms in a set divided by the number of terms. Sets don't have to be just numbers, they can be things like average age, or average height. Now let's look at an example of this:

Problem 36 (Example 1)

What is the mean of the numbers: 2, 3, 0, 3, 1, 4, 0, 3?

Proof. In this problem, the mean is also the average. To find the average, we have to take the sum of all the terms and divide it by the number of terms. The sum of all the terms is 16 divided by the 8 terms which makes the average $\boxed{2}$. □

These are just the basics, but there are more complicated problems. Specifically, we made this separate section for averages because they show up so frequently on the AMC 8. Now, let's look at another example with weighted average:

Problem 37

80% of my AMC 8 test scores are 24. The rest are 3. While I am inconsistent, I like to focus on the average. What is the average of my test scores?

Proof. Uh-oh! We don't know how many AMC 8 tests I got 24 on! Moreover, we don't even know the number of total AMC 8 tests I took! Thankfully, there is another way to do this. The 80% can be considered a "weight," indicating the proportion of the tests that I got 24 on. We can multiply the score I got (24) by the relative number of times I got that score (80% of the time), or the "weight," to find the amount that these good scores make up for in my average. We get $24 \cdot 80\% = 24 \cdot 0.8 = 19.2$. Similarly, we can find the amount that the scores of 3 make up by multiplying them by their relative frequency. I got a 3 20% of the time, so this makes up $3 \cdot 20\% = 3 \cdot 0.2 = 0.6$ of my average. Therefore, my average score on all of the AMC 8 tests I took is $19.2 + 0.6 = \boxed{19.8}$. □

Before we end the section, here is an extremely helpful problem solving tip when working with averages:

> **Remark 10.1.** When working with average problems, it is almost always helpful to write the averages in the problem as if you were about to calculate them. For example, if a problem says that the average of three numbers is 7, then let a_1, a_2, and a_3 be the three numbers (Adjust the variables to the needs of the problem. Specifically, if you are given other equations that tell you the relationships between the variables, account for this. You should write the given information as
> $$\frac{a_1 + a_2 + a_3}{3} = 7.$$
> It is also worth noting that given this information, one can find (by multiplying each side by 3) that
> $$a_1 + a_2 + a_3 = 21.$$
> At this point, you can substitute anything else that you know about the variables and solve for the answer.

To make this more concrete, let's try an example problem.

Problem 38

The average of three numbers is 3. The largest number is two times of the smaller number and the second largest number is one less than the largest. What is the largest number?

Proof. Let the three numbers be x, y, z from least to greatest. Then, the first sentence tells us that $\frac{x+y+z}{3} = 3$. Multiplying both sides by 3, we get $x + y + z = 9$. We also know, by the second sentence, that $z = 2x$ and $y = z - 1 = 2x - 1$. Substituting this into our sum, we find that $(x) + (2x - 1) + (2x) = 9$. Solving for x, we find $5x = 10$ or $x = 2$. We are tasked to find the largest number, which we know is $z = 2x$. We find $z = 2(2) = \boxed{4}$. $\qquad\square$

This last problem covers the majority of all complicated average problems on the AMC 8. Try these problems:

§10.1 Averages Problems

Problem 39 (Problem 3: AMC 8 2002)

What is the smallest possible average of four distinct positive even integers? (Hint: What is this set of numbers?)

Problem 40 (Problem 9: AMC 8 2004)

The average of the five numbers in a list is 54. The average of the first two numbers is 48. What is the average of the last three numbers?

Problem 41 (Problem 23: AMC 8 2000)

There is a list of seven numbers. The average of the first four numbers is 5, and the average of the last four numbers is 8. If the average of all seven numbers is $6\frac{4}{7}$, then the number common to both sets of four numbers is? (Hint: Set three variables: one to the sum of the first three numbers, one to the middle number, and one to the sum of the last three numbers. Now, write the given statements in mathematical language.)

Problem 42 (Problem 18: AMC 8 2002)

Gage skated 1 hr 15 min each day for 5 days and 1 hr 30 min each day for 3 days. How long would he have to skate the ninth day in order to average 85 minutes of skating each day for the entire time? $\left(\text{Hint: The average time for skating can be represented as } \frac{\text{total time spent skating}}{\text{total number of days}}.\right)$

§11 Venn Diagrams

Venn diagrams are an effective way to visualize comparisons between sets of numbers and data. They are drawn as two circles overlapping each other. Each individual circle corresponds to its own set of numbers or data. When combined, the overlapping part in the middle shows the common parts of the two sets. Every element of either set that sits in this area is shown to be common to both sets. Everything that is inside one of the circles but outside the other is shown to be apart of the first set but not the second. The most common Venn Diagrams are: two way Venn Diagrams and three way Venn Diagrams.

Let's look at a 2 way diagram first. Let our two sets be the set of 10th graders at a school and the set of band members in the school. If we plot our information in a Venn Diagram, we could first make a drawing of two circles with an overlap in between. Now, we can place our data into three sets: 10th graders who are not in band, band members who are not in 10th grade, and 10th graders who are also in band. We could list the names of the people in the first group in the circle labeled "10th graders," being sure to keep our list out of the circle labeled "band members." Similarly, we keep the data of the second group mentioned in the circle labeled "band members," making sure to keep out of the circle labeled "10th graders." In the middle of the two overlapping circles (in the overlap), we list out all of the people common to both sets, or the third mentioned group. What about all of the people in the school that are not in either group? We can choose to leave this group out of the picture, but if we wanted, we could list these people outside of both circles. This would show that the people belong to neither set.

Unlike a two way diagram, a three way diagram compares three different sets. An example of this would be listing owners of household pets by the pets that they own. The three household pets we can list are cats, dogs and birds. The area where the cats and dogs overlap (this means that the overlapping region of the circle labeled "cat owners" and the circle labeled "dog owners") is where an owner has both a cat and a dog (such an owner is listed here) (remember, this is regardless of whether a person owns a bird). The area where cats and birds meet is where an owner has a cat and a bird. The area where the bird and dog overlap is where an owner has a bird and a dog. The center most area, where all three circles overlap, is where an owner who has a cat, dog, and bird is listed.

Here is the basic routine when doing Venn Diagram problems:

> **Remark 11.1.** Work from the inside of a Venn Diagram to the outside and assign variables to the unknown parts of sets. Then, write equations down that you know to be true.

This isn't a very common problem type, so this problem basically sums it all up:

§11.1 Venn Diagrams Problems

Problem 43 (Problem 13: AMC 8 2007)

Sets A and B, shown in the Venn diagram, have the same number of elements. Their union has 2007 elements and their intersection has 1001 elements. Find the number of elements in A.

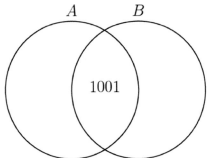

(Hint: "Union" means the entire set including both A and B, removing all duplicates of A and B. Basically, this is

part of A not in B+part of B not in A+common part to both A and B (intersection).

Use this formula by assigning variables to the unknown parts of the expression above.)

§12 Conversion Factors

Many times, we wish to convert between units. Say that we are trying to find how many feet are in 36 inches. We could intuitively find that we must divide by 12 to get $\frac{36}{12} = 3$ feet. However, this becomes much more complicated as the units become more complicated. For example, we could have wanted to convert centimeters to miles, or years to seconds. Sometimes on the AMC 8, we are presented with made-up units, making it extremely difficult to use this intuitive process. In these cases, we can use **conversion factors**. When using conversion factors, all we essentially do is multiply by 1 multiple times. To make this less abstract, we use the previous example as a starting point. We know that

$$1 \text{ foot} = 12 \text{ inches},$$

meaning that both $\frac{1 \text{ foot}}{12 \text{ inches}}$ and $\frac{12 \text{ inches}}{1 \text{ foot}}$ are equal to 1. This should be easy to understand after noticing that the numerator and denominator of these two fractions are the same length. This is where we start to "multiply by 1." We wanted to find the number of feet in 36 inches. If we multiply 36 inches to the first fraction we found above (which equals 1), we get

$$36 \text{ inches} \cdot \frac{1 \text{ foot}}{12 \text{ inches}}.$$

Notice that the value of 36 inches is maintained (because we are multiplying by 1). It turns out that in these types of computations, units such as feet, inches, seconds, and years can "cancel." Concretely, the inches in 36 inches cancels with the denominator of the fraction on the right that equals 1. When this happens, the inches unit essentially "disappears" and we are left with only feet. Doing the computation, we find that our product yields $\frac{36}{12}$ feet = 3 feet. Although this may have required much more thinking power than our first solution, this second solution is applicable to a much wider range of problems. For example, try the following problem.

Problem 44

Convert 4 years to seconds.

Proof. It is not easy to directly tell how many seconds are in one year, or even 1 day for that matter. This looks like a job for conversion factors. We know that

- 60 seconds = 1 minute;

- 60 minutes = 1 hour;

- 24 hours = 1 day;

- 365 days = 1 year.

Aha! We have, through a long set of facts, found a relationship between seconds and years. Because of all of these facts, we know that each of

35

- $\frac{60 \text{ seconds}}{1 \text{ minute}}$,

- $\frac{60 \text{ minutes}}{1 \text{ hour}}$,

- $\frac{24 \text{ hours}}{1 \text{ day}}$,

- $\frac{365 \text{ days}}{1 \text{ year}}$

are equal to 1. We notice that if we multiply all of these fractions, we are left with the unit $\frac{\text{seconds}}{\text{years}}$, while all other units cancel. Further, we notice that when we multiply this result to 4 years, our units become $\frac{\text{seconds}}{\text{years}} \cdot \text{years} = \text{seconds}$. Hence, we have found a clear path to the solution. If we multiply all of the fractions we just found by 4 years, we will get the number of seconds in 4 years. Let's try it:

$$\frac{60 \text{ seconds}}{1 \text{ minute}} \cdot \frac{60 \text{ minutes}}{1 \text{ hour}} \cdot \frac{24 \text{ hours}}{1 \text{ day}} \cdot \frac{365 \text{ days}}{1 \text{ year}} \cdot 4 \text{ years}.$$

As we just saw, all of the units except seconds will cancel and we will be left with (after all of the computation) the number of seconds in 4 years (as mentioned earlier). Multiplying, we get $\boxed{126144000 \text{ seconds}}$ to be our answer. That's a **lot** of seconds! $\qquad\square$

> **Remark 12.1.** Sources will often refer to what we call "Conversion Factors" as "Dimensional Analysis."

Let's try one harder problem:

> **Problem 45** (The Art of Problem Solving)
>
> If 4 gleeps are worth 3 glops and 2 glops are worth 5 glips, how many glips are worth the same as 10 gleeps?

Proof. We wish to find a way to convert from gleeps to glips. However, there is no direct relation between the two. Fortunately, we know that they are both related to glops, so maybe we can use conversion factors to solve the problem. Because of the given information, we know that each of

- $\frac{3 \text{ glops}}{4 \text{ gleeps}}$,

- $\frac{5 \text{ glips}}{2 \text{ glops}}$

are equal to 1. We find that if we multiply these two together, we get the units $\frac{\text{glips}}{\text{gleeps}}$. Further, we find that when we multiply by this result by 10 gleeps, we get glips as our unit. This is what we want, so we multiply them all. We get

$$10 \text{ gleeps} \cdot \frac{3 \text{ glops}}{4 \text{ gleeps}} \cdot \frac{5 \text{ glips}}{2 \text{ glops}} = \boxed{\frac{150}{8} \text{ glips}} = \boxed{18.75 \text{ glips}}.$$

□

Remark 12.2. Notice how

- $\frac{4 \text{ gleeps}}{3 \text{ glops}}$;

- $\frac{2 \text{ glops}}{5 \text{ glips}}$

are also equal to 1. Why did we not use these conversion factors instead? Well, the fractions that we chose allowed us to cancel all of the units, leaving only glips, which is what we wanted. Try using a different combination of fractions, including at least one of the two above. You will find that the units do not properly cancel, and therefore we cannot use any other combination of fractions to find the correct answer.

§12.1 Conversion Factors Problems

Problem 46 (The Art of Problem Solving)

Given that 1 inch is about 2.54 centimeters and 1 ounce is 28.35 grams, convert $16.2\text{in}^2\text{oz}^{-1}$ to centimeters and grams. (Hint: You will need to convert two units in this problem, inches and ounces to centimeters and grams, instead of just one. Also, note that $n^{-1} = \frac{1}{n}$.)

§13 Magic Grids

Remark 13.1. There is no good name to attribute to this section. To wit, by "Magic Grids," we mean to say "filling out grids," but this is not as catchy.

Magic Grid problems are extremely rare on the AMC 8. In these types of problems, test takers are given a grid of some sort with a type of rule on how to fill them out. We include these problems here only to give you a sense of the types of problems on the AMC 8. Here are two problems:

Problem 47 (Problem 9: AMC 8 2007)

To complete the grid below, each of the digits 1 through 4 must occur once in each row and once in each column. What number will occupy the lower right-hand square?

1		2	
2	3		
			4

Proof. This is a type of Sudoku puzzle! We just need to find the numbers in the fourth column or the fourth row. Then, we can use the process of elimination to find our answer. Since we already have one number in the first column, we try to find the numbers in the fourth column. We first note that the number in the first row, second column cannot be a 3, otherwise we would have two 3's in one column. Therefore, in order to have one 3 in the first row, the number in the first row, fourth column must be a 3. Now, we note that the number in the second row, fourth column cannot be a 2 or 3 because the second row already contains a 2 and 3. It also cannot be a 4 because the fourth column already has a 4. Therefore, the number in the second row, fourth column must be a 1. By the process of elimination on the fourth column, the number in the bottom right square must be 2. $\square$

See? That wasn't so hard! Even if this did feel a bit uncomfortable to you, do not worry (for the sake of math, try the problem again, but don't worry too much if you cannot understand). Let's try one more:

Problem 48 (Problem 11: AMC 8 2007)

Tiles I, II, III and IV are translated so one tile coincides with each of the rectangles A, B, C and D. In the final arrangement, the two numbers on any side common to two adjacent tiles must be the same. Which of the tiles is translated to Rectangle C?

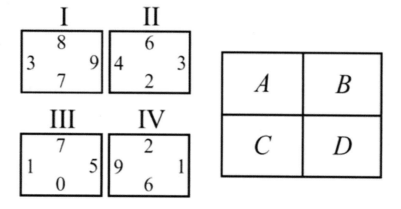

Proof. Instead of trying to find out the parts of the rectangles that coincide, we can focus on the parts of the rectangles that are facing outwards. Specifically, if we find a rectangle with two numbers that are not repeated, we can confidently place that rectangle in its correct spot. After some experimentation, we find that rectangle III has two numbers (0 and 5) that are not found anywhere else on any of the other rectangles. This means that these two sides must be facing outwards, because it is impossible to find rectangles that can coincide with these numbers. This can only happen if rectangle III is placed in position D. Therefore, the 1 on the left side of rectangle III must coincide with the 1 on the right of rectangle IV. So, rectangle $\boxed{IV}$ must be in position C. $\qquad\square$

And, that's it!

Part III
Number Theory in the AMC 8

§14 Introduction

Number Theory is the study of the relationships between numbers, specifically integers. In this unit, we will study how numbers work together and how they are built.

§15 Modular Arithmetic

We start off this unit by uncovering the mysteries of division. Specifically, we focus on the remainders.

Problem 49

Right now, it is 12:00 a.m. What time will it be in

- 5 hours?
- 12 hours?
- 17 hours?
- 24 hours?
- 29 hours?
- 65 hours?
- 245 hours?

Proof. In 5 hours, it will be $\boxed{5:00 \text{ a.m.}}$, which we can see without much difficulty.

In 12 hours, we will have been halfway through the day. So, it will have been $\boxed{12:00 \text{ p.m.}}$.

In 17 hours, it will have been 5 hours past the 12 hour mark. So, 5 hours past 12:00 p.m. is $\boxed{5:00 \text{ p.m.}}$.

In 24 hours, it will have been exactly one day after 12:00 a.m., so it will have been $\boxed{12:00 \text{ a.m.}}$, as two times that are one day apart have the same clock time.

In 29 hours, it will have been 5 hours past 12:00 a.m., our previous answer. So, it will have been $\boxed{5:00 \text{ a.m.}}$ again.

Before we attempt the 65 hours, we try and take advantage of the fact that two times that are one day apart have the same clock time. In other words, a clock will display the same time exactly one day after a certain time. In order to take advantage of this, we note that if we subtract 24 hours from 65 hours, we will have the same clock time as 65 hours from now. So, this is the same question as asking what time it will be after $65 - 24 = 41$ hours. Similarly, we can keep on subtracting multiples of 24 hours until we get a positive number that is less than 24. We get $65 - 24 \cdot 2 = 17$ hours. We already know that 17 hours after this initial time is $\boxed{5:00\text{p.m.}}$.

Similarly, we can subtract multiples of 24 from 245 to find that this is the same as finding the time after $245 - 24 \cdot 10 = 5$ hours. We know this already to be $\boxed{5:00\text{ a.m.}}$. $\qquad\square$

Although no time in history ever repeats, we were able to notice a repeating pattern in the time of a clock that allowed us to understand how to calculate our answers. Let's try a more technical problem founded on the same principles.

Problem 50

Imagine a circular spinner with numbers in a clockwise fashion in the order $0, 1, 2, 3, 0, 1, 2, 3, 0, \cdots$. Superman spun the spinner, starting from 0 and going to 1, and counted (really fast) that the spinner ticked, or moved clockwise one number, 1234 times (he's pretty strong too). What number did it land on?

Proof. We notice that the cycle repeats every 4 terms. So, we notice that the number after 1234 ticks is the same as the number after $1234 - 4 = 1230$ ticks. Similarly, we can keep on subtracting multiples of 4 in order to simplify the problem to a number of ticks under 4. We get $1234 - 308 \cdot 4 = 2$. so, this problem is the same as finding the number after 2 ticks. The number after 2 ticks is $\boxed{2}$. $\qquad\square$

In hindsight, this problem was the same as finding the remainder when 1234 was divided by 4. This is because the spinner repeats itself every 4 spins, so all that matters is how many spins one needs to do after all of the "groups of 4" in 1234. Let's define the modular function:

> **Definition 15.1** — When we divide a number a by a number b, we get a quotient q and remainder r such that $0 \leq r < b - 1$. Then, we can write our result as $a = b \cdot q + r$. We can write r as $a \pmod{b}$.

Along with this, let's define "congruence":

> **Definition 15.2** — Integers a and b are defined to be congruent with respect to modulus m if $a - b = k \cdot m$ for some integer m. This is written as $a \equiv b \pmod{m}$.

The $k \cdot m$ part just means that $a - b$ is a multiple of m. Let's explore this definition.

Problem 51

Explain why the congruence definition is the same as saying that a and b have the same remainder when divided by m.

Proof. Let us attempt this by proof by contradiction. Assume that a and b have different remainders c and d respectively such that

$$a = p \cdot m + c$$

and

$$b = q \cdot m + d.$$

Let's try to do $a - b$, since this is supposed to be a multiple of m. We get

$$a - b = (p - q) \cdot m + (c - d).$$

In order for the right hand side to be divisible by m, $c - d$ must also be divisible by m. Since $c \neq d$ and $0 \leq c, d < m$, it is impossible for $c - d$ to be divisible by m. This is a contradiction, meaning that we must have $c = d$. When this is true, the remainders cancel out in the above equation and we do indeed get a multiple of m when we compute $a - b$. $\square$

So, we have two interpretations now. Notice how we wrote a as $a = p \cdot m + c$ and b in a similar form. This will often come into handy when we try to prove other things in modular arithmetic. Before we get to the fun stuff, let's try out our new notation.

Problem 52

What is 65433 (mod 5)?

Proof. When we divide 65433 by 5, we get 13086 and a remainder of $\boxed{3}$, which we can write in the remainder form that we just learned as

$$65433 = 13086 \cdot 5 + 3.$$

Alternatively, we could have seen that all numbers that end in 0 or 5 are divisible by 5. So, we could have noted that since 65430 is a multiple of 5, our answer is $\boxed{3}$. $\square$

> **Remark 15.3.** Always be on the lookout for using divisibility tricks! We will learn more (not as obvious) divisibility tricks later.

One very obvious yet important identity to point out:

Problem 53

If $a \equiv b \pmod{m}$ and $b \equiv c \pmod{m}$, then prove that $a \equiv c \pmod{m}$.

Proof. The first given tells us that a and b have the same remainder $\pmod{m}$ while the second given tells us that b and c have the same remainder $\pmod{m}$. By the transitive property, we know that the remainder $\pmod{m}$ of a and c must be the same, so we conclude that $a \equiv c \pmod{m}$. $\qquad\square$

Now, the fun stuff. Let's get our hands dirty with some addition with mods.

Problem 54

Suppose that
$$a \equiv b \pmod{m}$$
and
$$c \equiv d \pmod{m}.$$
Prove that
$$a + c \equiv b + d \pmod{m}.$$

Proof. Let

- $a = p \cdot m + r$
- $b = q \cdot m + r$
- $c = x \cdot m + t$
- $d = y \cdot m + t$

where $0 \leq r, t < m$. Notice how the remainders for a and b are the same and c and d are the same. Now the solution is as straightforward as writing the statement that we wish to prove in this useful form:

$$(p \cdot m + r) + (x \cdot m + t) \equiv (q \cdot m + r) + (y \cdot m + t) \pmod{m}.$$

Now, we simplify both sides:

$$pm + r + xm + t \equiv qm + r + ym + t \pmod{m}.$$

We notice that the m terms on both sides an be disregarded as the $\pmod{m}$ only cares for the remainder when divided by m All of the m terms have remainder 0 when divided by m, so we get:

$$r + t \equiv r + t \pmod{m}.$$

Since all steps are reversible, we can conclude that

$$a + c \equiv b + d \pmod{m}.$$

□

Looking back, we see that we need not focus on the m terms at all, even from the start. They can be disregarded as the sum (that we later manually compute) will simply result in a term that is divisible by m. So, removing the m terms on the left side product all together, we get rt right away. Now, let's see a specific case of this.

Problem 55

Suppose that

$$a \equiv b \pmod{m}.$$

Prove that

$$a + c \equiv b + c \pmod{m}$$

for some constant c.

Proof. As mentioned before, this is a specific case of the last problem. Since $c \equiv c \pmod{m}$, we have

$$a \equiv b \pmod{m}$$

and

$$c \equiv c \pmod{m}.$$

From the last problem, we know that

$$a + c \equiv b + c \pmod{m}.$$

□

This means that similar to an equation, a constant can be added to both sides of a congruence statement as this does not affect the difference of the remainders of the two sides. You will be asked to prove as part of the problems that this is also true for subtraction. As a hint, it is essentially the same proof we did here. Let's use this result in practice.

Problem 56

Find the units digit of

$$123456789543234567 + 653367654321 + 123467876543.$$

Proof. I am certainly not computing **that**. Not even with a calculator. What is an easier way to do this? We want the units digit of a number. This is the same as taking the modulus of the number with respect to 10 (make sure you see this). The first number is congruent to 7 (mod 10), the second number is congruent to 1 (mod 10), and the third number is congruent to 3 (mod 10). We just found a couple problems ago that the (mod 10) of the sum of these numbers is the same as the sum of the individual moduli. We get that the units digit of the sum is the same as the units digit of $7 + 1 + 3 = 11$. So our answer is $\boxed{1}$. $\square$

> **Remark 15.4.** The units digit of a sum is the sum of the last digits of the addends. This can be quite important to remember in competitions.

Onto multiplication.

Problem 57

Suppose that
$$a \equiv b \pmod{m}$$
and
$$c \equiv d \pmod{m}.$$
Prove that
$$ac \equiv bd \pmod{m}.$$

Proof. Similar to the addition version of this proof, let

- $a = p \cdot m + r$
- $b = q \cdot m + r$
- $c = x \cdot m + t$
- $d = y \cdot m + t$

where $0 \leq r, t < m$. Again, notice how the remainders for a and b are the same and c and d are the same. Again, we simply substitute our values into the statement we wish to prove true:
$$(p \cdot m + r)(x \cdot m + t) \equiv (q \cdot m + r)(y \cdot m + t) \pmod{m}.$$

Before we expand this, we think about these products. The factors all contain one m term. When we multiply both sides out (try this for yourself), these m terms will multiply with other terms to form m terms (obviously). Therefore, the only product that is not an m term is the product of the terms in both factors that are not already m terms, namely r and t. So, we can disregard all of the m terms and we end up with rt on both sides. So, we get

$$rt \equiv rt \pmod{m}.$$

Since this is obviously true and all our steps are reversible, we know that

$$ac \equiv bd \pmod{m}.$$

$\square$

Again, we try to focus on a specific case of this proof:

Problem 58

Suppose that
$$a \equiv b \pmod{m}.$$

Prove that
$$ac \equiv bc \pmod{m}.$$

Proof. We know that
$$c \equiv c \pmod{m}$$

and the given
$$a \equiv b \pmod{m}.$$

Then, by the last problem,
$$ac \equiv bc \mod m.$$

$\square$

> **Remark 15.5.** Make sure you understand the intuition of this problem. This will make many future problems and concepts easier to grasp.

This means that we can also multiply both sides of a congruence statement by a number. Note that division does not necessarily work in modular arithmetic (only in certain special cases). We can extend this proof to show that exponentiation works for a congruence statement as well.

Problem 59

Suppose that
$$a \equiv b \pmod{m}.$$

Prove that
$$a^n \equiv b^n \pmod{m}.$$

Proof. Writing the given statement twice, we know that

$$a \equiv b \pmod{m}$$

and

$$a \equiv b \pmod{m}.$$

We write this twice because now we can multiply the two respective sides. We get that $a^2 \equiv b^2 \pmod{m}$. We write this along with the original given statement of the problem:

$$a^2 \equiv b^2 \pmod{m}$$

and

$$a \equiv b \pmod{m}.$$

Similar to last time, we can multiply the respective sides to get that $a^3 \equiv b^3 \pmod{m}$. Similarly, we can keep on doing this over and over again. Specifically, if $a^k \equiv b^k \pmod{m}$ (we have shown a couple of k for which this is true already), then writing this along with the given statement, we find:

$$a^k \equiv b^k \pmod{m}$$

and

$$a \equiv b \pmod{m}.$$

Combining these two, we find that $a^{k+1} \equiv b^{k+1} \pmod{m}$. And thus we have that

$$a^n \equiv b^n \pmod{m}.$$

$\square$

Problem 60

Evaluate
$$39^{12345} + 35^{12345} \pmod{37}.$$

Proof. Even if I had a super calculator and wanted to waste 5 minutes of my life, I could not compute that. There must be a better way of doing this. We try to take the $\pmod{37}$ of both terms in the sum. We know that $39 \pmod{37} = 2$, but $35 \pmod{37}$ is just 35. That is not helpful. However, we notice that both 35 and 39 are equidistant from 37, so we try to take advantage of this. We find that $35 \equiv -2 \pmod{37}$ because it is just short of 37.

> **Remark 15.6.** It is often useful to look at the negative modulus of a number. Especially when power sums show up, as they do here.

Replacing 39 with 2 and 35 with -2 because these are congruent, we find that the original question is

$$2^{12345} + (-2)^{12345} \pmod{37}.$$

Aha! We notice the negative sign as an opportunity. We take out the negative sign:

$$2^{12345} - 2^{12345} \pmod{37}.$$

This is just 0! So the answer is $\boxed{0}$. $\qquad\square$

> **Remark 15.7.** The reason that we were able to substitute 2 for 39 and -2 for 35 is because we know that
> $$39 \equiv 2 \pmod{37}$$
> and
> $$35 \equiv -2 \pmod{37}.$$
> So, when we raise both sides of both congruence statements to the 12345th power, we find that
> $$39^{12345} \equiv 2^{12345} \pmod{37}$$
> and
> $$35^{12345} \equiv -2^{12345} \pmod{37}.$$
> Since the left sides of both congruence statements are the numbers we find in the problem, we are allowed to make the substitution. Using similar logic, we find that we can substitute numbers that are congruent in these types of sums when a certain number is raised to a power.

Now let's try a slightly more applicable approach to these types of modular arithmetic problems.

Problem 61 (The Art of Problem Solving)

Find the remainder when 5^{2005} is divided by 7.

Proof. Let's see if we can find a pattern in the powers of 5. We see that $5 \equiv 5 \pmod{7}$. Additionally, $5^2 = 25 \equiv 4 \pmod{7}$. In order to find $5^3 \pmod{7}$, we can (instead of just computing it) take the value that we got for 25 $\pmod{7}$ and multiply this by 5. So, 5^3 $\pmod{7}$ is $4 \cdot 5 = 20 \equiv -1 \pmod{7}$. We wish to find an easy number as we continue. Something like 1. We have -1, and we notice that the square of this is 1. So, we find that $(5^3)^2 = 5^6 \equiv (-1)^2 = 1 \pmod{7}$. So, if we can divide the given power that 5 is raised to, or 2005, into groups of 5^6, then we can simply "multiply by 1" and reduce our problem. Specifically,

$$5^{2005} = 5^{6 \cdot 344 + 1} = 5^{6 \cdot 344} \cdot 5^1 = (5^6)^{344} \cdot 5^1 \equiv 1^{344} \cdot 5^1 = \boxed{5} \mod 7.$$

$\qquad\square$

Remark 15.8. A little experimentation goes a long way!

Problem 62

Find the units digit of 9^{8^7}.

Proof. Recall that finding the units digit is the same as taking 9^{8^7} (mod 10). Since $9 \equiv -1$ (mod 10), this problem becomes the same as finding $(-1)^{8^7}$ (mod 10). The number $(-1)^{8^7}$ could either be -1 or 1. This depends on the value of 8^7 and whether this is odd or even. If 8^7 is even, then our answer is 1, while if 8^7 is odd, then our answer is -1. This is because when we raise -1 to an even power, we get 1. On the other hand, if we raise -1 to an odd power, we will get -1. So, is 8^7 odd or even? Well, we can take $8^7 \equiv 0^7 = 0$ (mod 2) to find that 8^7 is indeed even. Therefore, our answer is $\boxed{1}$. □

Again, we see the usefulness of negative moduli.

§15.1 Parity

In this section, we focus on a specific modulus: modulus with respect to 2. The modulus with respect to 2 tells us whether a number is even or odd. We call this a number's "parity." We will now explore the addition and multiplication properties with respect to modulus 2.

Problem 63

What is the parity of the sum of an even number and another even number? An even number and an odd number? An odd number and another odd number?

Proof. In the first question, an even number is congruent to 0 (mod 2), so adding two odd numbers in (mod 2) gives $0 + 0 = 0$ (mod 2). Therefore, the sum of an even number and another even number is always $\boxed{\text{even}}$.

Similarly, the sum of an odd and even number in (mod 2) is $1 + 0 = 1$ (mod 2). Therefore, the sum of an even and odd number is always $\boxed{\text{odd}}$.

Once again, the sum of two odd numbers in (mod 2) is $1 + 1 = 2 \equiv 0$ (mod 2). Therefore, the sum of two odd numbers is always $\boxed{\text{even}}$. □

These facts are worth memorizing and can help out often. However, even if you can't remember them, they are only a simple derivation away! Or, you could try out an example and see what you find. It turns out that the above statements are also true for subtraction. For example, the first fact presented in the problem above, converted to subtraction, would become: the difference of two even numbers is even. The same can be said for the other two facts above. Now, onto multiplication:

Problem 64

What is the parity of the product of two even numbers? One even number and one odd number? Two odd numbers?

Proof. Two even numbers, each congruent to 0 (mod 2) will have a product congruent to $0 \cdot 0 = 0$ (mod 2). This means that the product of two even numbers is always even.

The product of one even number and one odd number is congruent to $0 \cdot 1 = 0$ (mod 2). This means that the product of an even number and an odd number is even.

Similarly, the product of two odd numbers is congruent to $1 \cdot 1 = 1$ (mod 2). This means that the product of two odd numbers is always odd. □

Sadly, this does not work for division. Parity, as said before, can be quite useful, so it is useful to memorize these or at least understand them well enough to some back to them quickly. They are important especially when it comes to prime numbers. We will learn more about primes later, but for now:

Problem 65

The only even prime is 2. All other primes are odd. If I know that the sum of two primes is odd, then what is true about the two numbers?

Proof. We know that if the sum of two numbers is odd, then one number must be even while the other is odd. Since the only even prime is 2, we know that this must be the even prime number of interest, while the other number can be any prime other than 2. □

This last problem arises quite frequently in competitions, so keep a look out! Note that the same thing that we did with parity can be done for any modulus, but we show parity because it is so common.

§15.2 Modular Arithmetic Problems

Problem 66

Suppose that
$$a \equiv b \pmod{m}$$
and
$$c \equiv d \pmod{m}.$$
Prove that
$$a - c \equiv b - d \pmod{m}.$$

Problem 67

Suppose that
$$a \equiv b \pmod{m}.$$
Using the last problem, prove that
$$a - c \equiv b - c \pmod{m}$$
for some constant c.

Problem 68 (The Art of Problem Solving)

Find the units digit of 7^{7^7}. (You can search up the answer to verify your solution.)

Problem 69 (Problem 14: AMC 8 2000)

What is the units digit of $19^{19} + 99^{99}$? (Hint: Try $\pmod{10}$.)

Problem 70 (Problem 8: AMC 8 2005)

Suppose m and n are positive odd integers. Which of the following must also be an odd integer? (Hint: Consider parity.)

(A) $m + 3n$ **(B)** $3m - n$ **(C)** $3m^2 + 3n^2$ **(D)** $(nm + 3)^2$ **(E)** $3mn$

§16 Converting Bases

In this section, we will go over converting bases, so that it will become easy to convert between given bases. Why do we use decimal notation for numbers (aka base 10)? It is because we only have 10 fingers. Now imagine if we had only 5 fingers or even 16 fingers. As such, converting bases is a very important and aesthetic concept. Another reason why it is important is because computers operate in base 2, so they only recognize the digits 0 and 1. This is called binary. To understand what computers are saying makes it important to be able to convert between number bases. Now, let's look at how to convert bases.

Problem 71

Convert 32_{10} to base 2.

Proof. To start off, the most fool-proof way is to divide. When I say divide, I mean:

- Divide the given number in base 10 into the base you want to convert into. Also make sure to write the remainder.

- Keep going until the number that you get is smaller than the target base.

- Then, you take the remainders from the bottom up and write it as your answer.

So first we need to:

- $32 = 16 \cdot 2 + 0$, so the remainder is 0;

- $16 = 84 \cdot 2 + 0$, so the remainder is 0;

- $8 = 4 \cdot 2 + 0$, so the remainder is 0;

- $4 = 2 \cdot 2 + 0$, so the remainder is 0;

- $2 = 1 \cdot 2 + 0$, so the remainder is 0;

- $1 = 0 \cdot 2 + 1$, so the remainder is 1.

At this point, the number 0 from dividing 2 from 1 is smaller than 0. This means that we have finished dividing. Now, after the dividing the numbers, rather than looking at the quotient, we need to look at the remainder. When writing the answer down, we have to start from the bottom up. Because base 2 is not written in numbers like base 10, it is a list of 0s and 1s. When writing the answer, we look at the last remainder which is 1 and make our way down, so the answer is $\boxed{100000_2}$.

Now, to make sure that we got the correct answer, we must convert the answer in base 2 back into base 10. When reading binary, we have to read it in terms of powers of 2. The first term corresponds to 2^0. The second term will be equals to 2^1, and the next number will be 2^2 and so on. Also, when we have a zero, it means that the number will not be included, just like the zeros in 10000000 don't account for any part of the number. On the other hand, if we have a 1, then it contributes to the value of the number. When you find a number that you must include, then we have to add it onto our total. A very big mistake that people make is that they read the answer from right to left to right. This is wrong, we need to read the answer from right to left. This means that the 0th term will be the right most term and increasing towards the left, and the value corresponding to these digits increases as we go from right to left.

Now, let's look at our problem. The answer we got was 100000_2. So now, let's make our way through the number. The first position will be 2^0, or 1. Because there is a 0 there, we do not need to include it in our total. The next position will be 2^1, or 2. This position also has a 0 so we do not need to include it. We have zeros for the 3rd, 4th, and 5th positions so 2^2, or 4, 2^3, or 8, and 2^4 or 16, will not be included as part of the value of the number. Now, we go onto the 6th position. This position has a 1 which means that it must be added to our total value. The sixth position's value will be 2^5, or 32. Because our total until now was 0, we add $32 + 0$, which gives us $\boxed{32}$. This was our original number so we got the answer correct. $\qquad\square$

Problem 72

Convert 110_{10} to base 16.

Proof. After looking at how to convert a number from base 10 to base 2, now let's look at how to convert a number from base 10 to base 16. There is one fundamental difference about base 16 and the other bases. This difference is that when using the dividing method that was specified in the problem above, a remainder containing two digits can show up. Because two digits are not allowed (as we only have space for one digit in each slot), a slightly different technique is used. Now, let's solve our problem. To start off, we must begin by using the same dividing technique:

- $110 = 16 \cdot 66 + 14$; So the remainder is 14.

- $6 = 16 \cdot 60 + 6$; So the remainder is 6.

This division is relatively short, but the problem that was pointed out earlier can be seen. The remainder in the first division is 14 which is a 2 digit number. When this comes up, the way to write this down is relatively simple. We replace the two digit numbers with a letter. 10 should be replaced with an A. 11 should be replaced with a B. 12 should be replaced with a C, and so on until we get to 15, which should be replaced with a F. Now, we look the number at hand, which is 14. If you follow the pattern, 14 should be replaced with an E. Just like binary, where we read from bottom up, for all the numbers, we read bottom up. So the last remainder is a 6 and 14 is replaced with an E so our answer is $\boxed{6E_{16}}$. $\qquad\square$

Problem 73

Convert 140_{10} into base 8.

Proof. Following the principle of dividing, we need to divide the 140 into 8 multiple times. Now let's divide:

- $140 = 8 \cdot 17 + 4$, so the remainder is 4.

- $17 = 8 \cdot 2 + 1$, so the remainder is 1

- $2 = 8 \cdot 0 + 2$, so the remainder is 2.

Just like in base 16 and base 2, we need to take the answer from the remainders going bottom up. So our answer will be $\boxed{214_8}$. $\qquad\square$

Problem 74

Convert 85_{10} into base 9.

Proof. Just like how we have done so far, we will use the dividing method. Now let's start dividing:

- $485 = 9 \cdot 9 + 4$, so the remainder is 4;

- $9 = 9 \cdot 1 + 0$, so the remainder is 0;

After dividing, we have to look from bottom up and so we get the answer $\boxed{4_9}$. $\qquad\square$

After solving problems about converting numbers from base 10 into the other bases, we will now look at how to convert from a base (that is not 10) into base 10.

Problem 75

Convert 3456_7 into base 10.

Proof. The process of converting from base 7 into 10 is very simple. All we have to do is take the individual digits from the whole number and multiply them by the base to the corresponding powers of the base minus one.

Let's look at our number of 3456. When I say 'split' the number I mean take the individual digits. So, we must take 3 and multiply it by the corresponding power of 7 which is 3 so we get $3 \cdot 7^3$. Next, we take the next digit which is 4 and multiple it by the corresponding power of 7 which is 2. This gives us $4 \cdot 7^2$. Next, we move onto 5 and multiply it by one less power of 7 so we get $5 \cdot 7^1$. Finally, we have to deal with 6, to which we multiply the corresponding power of 7, which gives us $6 \cdot 7^0$. After gathering all of our results, we have to add them up, so we get $3 \cdot 7^3 + 3 \cdot 7^2 + 3 \cdot 7^1 + 3 \cdot 7^0$. After adding all of these up, we get $\boxed{1266}$. $\qquad\square$

§16.1 Converting Bases Problems

Problem 76

Convert 85_{10} into base 9.

Problem 77 (Problem 19: AMC 10 2013)

In base 10, the number 2013 ends in the digit 3. In base 9, on the other hand, the same number is written as $(2676)_9$ and ends in the digit 6. For how many positive integers b does the base-b-representation of 2013 end in the digit 3?

§17 Prime Numbers

Definition 17.1 — Prime numbers are numbers which have divisors of 1 and itself.

Let's look at some prime numbers.

Problem 78

Find the first 15 prime numbers.

Proof. So the first prime number is 2 because its factors are itself and 1. Although 1 can be considered as a prime number, it cannot be considered one because its factor is itself. You need to multiply 1 by 1 to get 1, and because both factors are one, it cannot be considered a prime number. Then we move onto 3, which has divisors of 3 and 1. Continuing like this, the next few prime numbers are 5, 7, 11, 13, 17, 19, 23, 29, 31, 37, 41, 43, 47. So, if we look at the first 15 prime numbers in this list, we get $\boxed{2, 3, 5, 7, 11, 13, 17, 19, 23, 29, 31, 37, 41, 43, 47}$. $\square$

Because of the case that prime numbers are divisible by 1 and itself, prime numbers are considered considered special. When find the divisors of a number, one of the most common methods is to use prime factorization.

Definition 17.2 — The fundamental theorem of arithmetic states that every number greater that one is a prime number or can be shown as a product of prime numbers.

Like stated in the fundamental theorem of arithmetic, we can split up a number into prime numbers. This is called prime factorization. One of the ways to prime factorize a number is to use a factorization tree. The factorization tree is a common method by which we represent the prime factors of a number using 'tree branches'. When writing a number based on its prime factors, if there is more than the same number, we write as an exponent, and keep multiplying the factors. For example if a number's prime factors are: 2, 2, 2, 3, 5, we can write this as $2^3 \, 3 \cdot 5$. Now, let's try to prime factorize a number:

Problem 79

Prime factorize 81.

Proof. The number that we must prime factorize is 81. Now, let us use a method similar to the prime factorization tree. First, we have to look at ways to divide 81. The most common would be $9 \cdot 9$. After we split 81 into $9 \cdot 9$, we have to split the nines even further. The nines divide into $3 \cdot 3$. This is the furthest we can go because 3 is a prime number and we cannot prime factorize a number which is already prime. Now, we look at the last factors in the group, and replace with the numbers at the bottom of the tree, or the most broken down form of the number. They would be the four threes. So the prime factorization of 81 answer would be $\boxed{3^4}$ □

Problem 80

Prime factorize 256.

Proof. Like the last time, we will continuously divide 256 by numbers that we know are divisors, until all that we are left with are prime numbers at the bottom of our 'tree'. The most obvious case to solving this would be to divide 256 by 2 and we keep doing so until we get 1. Another not so obvious case is the fact that 256 is the square of 16 so we can write it in this way as well. We shall go through both cases.

First, let's divide 256 by 2, which gives us: 128. Then we divide 128 by 2, which is: 64. Then we divide 64 by 2 which is: 32. We keep going, dividing 32 by 2, which is: 16, then dividing 16 by 2 which is: 8, then 8 by 2 which is: 4, and then finally 4 by 2 which is: 2. Now, we look at all the branches for the prime numbers. The only prime number that divides this number is 2. There are eight twos so we can write the answer as $\boxed{2^8}$.

Now, we look at dividing 256 by its square roots. So, 256 can be written as $16 \cdot 16$. We can divide 16 into $4 \cdot 4$. Now, we have 4 base branches at the bottom of the tree. Next, we divide the fours into $2 \cdot 2$. Now we have 8 base branches(It is often helpful to sketch out these branches on paper). This means that there are eight twos which one again gives us the answer of $\boxed{2^8}$

□

Problem 81

Prime Factorize 12.

Proof. Just like we have been doing, we will divide 12 by its prime factors. We shall start with the easiest factor to recognize is 2. We find that $\frac{12}{2} = 6$. Then, we divide 6 into 2 and 3. This is the most that we can do, as all of the numbers at the base of our tree are prime. So, we have two twos and one three, so we can write our answer as $\boxed{2^2 \cdot 3}$. □

Now, we will be moving onto counting divisors. Counting divisors is the process of finding the number of divisors that can divide into a given number. Now, let's look at a problem:

Problem 82

Find the number of divisors from 54.

Proof. In this problem, we will be prime factorizing 54 first. We can start off by splitting 54 into $9 \cdot 6$. We can split the 9 into $3 \cdot 3$ and we can split the 6 into $2 \cdot 3$. Now, we count the number of divisors in the tree, as the numbers at the bottom of our tree are all prime. We have three 3's and one 2 which can be written as $3^3 \cdot 2^1$.

After looking at this, we can replace the 3 in the power of 3 with a and replace 1 in the power of 2 with b. All divisors of 54 must be in the form $3^a \cdot 2^b$, where $a \le 3$ and $b \le 1$. a has to be less than or equal to 3, and b has to be less than or equal to one because that is the power. We know that a has values of 0, 1, 2, and 3, while b has values of 0 and 1. We know that a has 4 possible values while b has 3 so we just multiply the two giving us the number of factors. a can have 4 values and b can have 2 so $4 \cdot 2 = \boxed{8}$ divisors of 54. These divisors of 54 are 1,2,3,6,9,18,27,and 54. □

Problem 83

Find the number of divisors from 12.

Proof. Just like the last problem, we will be splitting 12 into its prime factors. The prime factors of 12 are $2^2 \cdot 3$. We can re-write the 3 as 3^1. After this, we replace the 2 in the exponent with a and the 1 in the exponent with b. All divisors of 12 must be in the form $2^a \cdot 3^b$, where $a \le 2$ and $b \le 1$. Now, because $a \le 2$, the possible values of a are 0, 1, and 2. $b \le 1$, so the possible values of b are 0, and 1. Now, like the last problem, we take the number of choices in the power which is 3 for a, and 2 for b. Multiplying these two, the number of factors for 12 are $\boxed{6}$. □

§17.1 Prime Number Problems

Problem 84

Prime factorize 36.

Problem 85

Prime factorize 72.

Problem 86

Find the number of divisors for 256.

§18 GCD

> **Definition 18.1** — The gcd, also known as the "Greatest Common Divisor", is a term used when we have to find the greatest common factor of multiple numbers.

Like the fundamental theorem of arithmetic states, all numbers greater than one are prime numbers or products of prime numbers. The same can also be said about a number's factors. Because of this reason, we can use prime factorization to find factors of multiple numbers. Here are the steps:

- First prime factorize both numbers.

- Find the common prime factors amongst both prime factorization trees.

- Take the highest power that any prime in the prime factorizations of both numbers that both numbers are divisible by

Problem 87

Find $\gcd(12, 10)$.

Proof. Like the steps mentioned, we first have to prime factorize 12 and 10. First, lets prime factorize 12. We can split up 12 into $3 \cdot 4$. After that, we can split 4 further into $2 \cdot 2$. So, the prime factors for 12 are $2 \cdot 2 \cdot 3$. Now, we need to prime factorize 10. We can split 10 into $2 \cdot 5$. Now that we have the prime factors for both numbers, we can move onto the next step.

Now, we need to find the common numbers in both factors. Comparing $2 \cdot 2 \cdot 3$ and $2 \cdot 5$, we find that there is only one 2 in common between both sets of factors. We can then conclude that the gcd for 12 and 10 is $\boxed{2}$. $\qquad\square$

Problem 88

Find gcd(54, 36).

Proof. The first step in finding the gcd is to prime factorize both numbers. First, lets prime factorize 54. We can split up 54 into $9 \cdot 6$. We can split 9 even further into $3 \cdot 3$. We can also split 6 into $2 \cdot 3$. After doing this, we get that the prime factors for 54 are $2 \cdot 3 \cdot 3 \cdot 3$. Now, we need to prime factorize 36. We can split 36 into $6 \cdot 6$. We can then split both sixes into $2 \cdot 3$. We now get that the prime factors of 36 are $2 \cdot 2 \cdot 3 \cdot 3$.

Now, we need to find the common factors between the factors of 54, which are, $2 \cdot 3 \cdot 3 \cdot 3$ and the factors of 90, which are, $2 \cdot 2 \cdot 3 \cdot 3$. As we can see, the factors of 54 has three, threes and 36 has two threes. This means that there are two threes in common. Next, we can move on to the twos. There is one two in 54 and two, twos in 36. This means that there is one two that is in common. Now that we have all the factors, we just need to multiply them. Multiplying $2 \cdot 3 \cdot 3$, we get that the gcd of 54 and 36 is $\boxed{18}$. $\qquad\square$

Problem 89

Find gcd(81, 90).

Proof. We first need to prime factorize 81 and 90. Starting to prime factorize 81, we can split up 81 into $9 \cdot 9$. We can split both nines further into $3 \cdot 3$. This gives us the prime factors of $3 \cdot 3 \cdot 3 \cdot 3$. Next, we need to prime factorize 90. We can split 90 into $9 \cdot 10$. We can then split up the 10 into, $2 \cdot 5$. This gives us the prime factors of $2 \cdot 3 \cdot 5$.

Next, we have to find the common factors between the factors of 81 which are $3 \cdot 3 \cdot 3 \cdot 3$, and the factors of 90 which are $2 \cdot 3 \cdot 5$. The common number is 3 and 3. Now, after multiplying $3 \cdot 3$, we now know that the gcd of 81 and 90 is $\boxed{9}$ $\qquad\square$

Problem 90

Find gcd(12, 18, 20).

Proof. Just like the last few problems, we have to prime factorize the three numbers. We already know that 12 prime factorized is $2 \cdot 2 \cdot 3$. We can prime factorize 18 by splitting it up into $9 \cdot 2$. Then we can split up 9 into $3 \cdot 3$. This gives is $3 \cdot 3 \cdot 2$. Next, we need to split up 20 into $5 \cdot 4$. We can then split up 4 into $2 \cdot 2$. This gives us $5 \cdot 2 \cdot 2$.

Now that we have all the factors of 12 which are, $2 \cdot 2 \cdot 3$, the factors of 18 which are, $3 \cdot 3 \cdot 2$, and the factors of 20 which are $5 \cdot 2 \cdot 2$. Now, we need to take the common factors of all three numbers. The common factors is one two. After find the common factors out of all three numbers, we get that the gcd of 12, 18, and 20 is $\boxed{2}$. □

§18.1 GCD Practice Problems

Problem 91

Find gcd(10, 5).

Problem 92

Find gcd(100, 120).

Problem 93

Find gcd(130, 190).

Problem 94

Find gcd(56, 84).

§19 LCM

> **Definition 19.1** — The lcm, also known as the "Least Common Multiple", is a term used when we have to find the least common multiple of multiple numbers.

Now, we will move onto finding the lcm. lcm stands for "The Least Common Multiple." Like the name states, we are supposed to find the smallest number that is a multiple of the two given numbers. Like the steps for find the gcd, we will need to find the prime factors for all the numbers. Here are the steps:

- Find the prime factors for both numbers.

- Pair off any common factors. Now, multiply these common divisors in the pair once in addition to any unique prime divisors. This is the lcm. For example, if the first number has one 3, and the second has two 3's, then you must take the two threes.

- After taking count of the greatest number of times each factor appears in either number, you multiply all of the factors you just found, giving you the LCM

Problem 95

Find lcm(12, 10).

Proof. The first step is to prime factorize. Let's start with 12. 12 can be split up into $3 \cdot 4$. We can than split 4 into $2 \cdot 2$. Now, we get that the prime factors of 12 are $2 \cdot 2 \cdot 3$. Next, we need to split 10. We can split 10 into $2 \cdot 5$.

We now have the prime factors for 12, which is $2 \cdot 2 \cdot 3$ and we the factors 10 which is $2 \cdot 5$. Looking at this, we can now move onto our next step. We now have to look at each factor and find the highest amount of times it appears in each number. We then take the number of factors which are more prominent. We will first start with 2: 2 appears twice in 12 and once in 10. The most prominent is the two, 2's in 12, so we have two, 2's. Then we move onto to 3: There is only one 3 in 12 and no 3 10. This means that we need to take the one three in 12. Next, we move onto the 5: There is only one 5 in 10, and no 5 in 12, so we only have one 5. Taking the two, 2's, one 3, and one 5, if we multiply them, we get the lcm of 12 and 10. Multiplying $2 \cdot 2 \cdot 3 \cdot 5$, gives us the lcm of 12 and 10 as $\boxed{60}$. $\square$

Problem 96

Find lcm(9, 4).

Proof. First, we need to find the prime factors of 9 and 4. Starting with 9, we can split it up into $3 \cdot 3$. Next, we can split up the 4 into $2 \cdot 2$.

Now, we can move onto the next step. There are two 3's in 9 but zero threes in 4 so we have two 3's. Then, we have two, 2's in 4 but zero 2's in 9 so we have two 2's. If we multiply $2 \cdot 2 \cdot 3 \cdot 3$, we get that the lcm for 9 and 4 is $\boxed{36}$. $\square$

Problem 97

Find lcm(36, 54).

Proof. The first step is to prime factorize 36 and 54. First, we can split 36 into $6 \cdot 6$. We can split both sixes into $2 \cdot 3$. This gives us $2 \cdot 2 \cdot 3 \cdot 3$. Next, we can split 54 into $9 \cdot 6$. We can then split the nine into $3 \cdot 3$ and the 6 into $2 \cdot 3$. With this, we get that the prime factors of 54 are $3 \cdot 3 \cdot 3 \cdot 2$.

We need to now take the greatest number of factors from each number. Starting with 2: We have two, 2's in 36 and one 2 in 54, so we get two, 2's. Next, we have two 3's in 36 and three, 3's in 54. If we multiply $2 \cdot 2 \cdot 3 \cdot 3 \cdot 3$, we get that the lcm of 54 and 36 is $\boxed{108}$. $\square$

Problem 98

Find lcm(18, 20).

Proof. First, we need to prime factorize 18 and 20. We can start by splitting 18 into $2 \cdot 9$. We can then split the 9 into $3 \cdot 3$. Next we can split 20 into $4 \cdot 5$. Then we can split the four into $2 \cdot 2$. With this, we get that the prime factors for 20 are $2 \cdot 2 \cdot 5$. This gives us the factors for 20 which are $2 \cdot 3 \cdot 3$.

Now, we need to find the greatest number of factors from each number. We can start off with 2. There are two, 2's in 20 and one two in 18, which gives us two, 2's. Next, we have one 5 in 20 and zero 5 in 18 which gives us one 5. If we move on, get zero 3's in 20 and two in 18 so we get two 3's in 18, so we have two threes. If we multiply $2 \cdot 2 \cdot 5 \cdot 3 \cdot 3$, we get that the lcm for 18 and 20 is $\boxed{180}$. $\square$

§19.1 LCM Practice Problems

Problem 99

Find lcm(20, 36).

Problem 100

Find lcm(10, 26).

Problem 101

Find lcm(56, 72).

§20 Euclidean Algorithm

Finding the gcd of two numbers a and b can be done by comparing the prime factorizations of the two numbers. However, there is an even better way to find the $\gcd(a, b)$. We start by proving a lemma.

Conjecture 20.1 (Discovering the Euclidean Algorithm)

If a and b are nonzero integers and k is an integer, then $\gcd(a, b) = \gcd(a, b - k \cdot a)$.

Proof. It suffices to show that the $\gcd(a,b)$ divides $b - k \cdot a$. If $d = \gcd(a,b)$, then $a = d \cdot x$ and $b = d \cdot y$ for some x and y. Note that because $d = \gcd(a,b)$, x and y must be **relatively prime**, meaning that $\gcd(x,y) = 1$. Thus,

$$b - k \cdot a = (d \cdot y) - k \cdot (d \cdot x) = d(y - k \cdot x).$$

Therefore, $b - k \cdot a$ is also a multiple of d. Therefore, we must have $\gcd(a,b) = \gcd(a, b - k \cdot a)$. $\qquad\square$

How does this help us find the $\gcd(a,b)$ for two integers a and b? Well, this helps us to simplify the problem, as shown in the following example:

Problem 102 (Euclidean Algorithm Example)

Find the $\gcd(144, 270)$.

Proof. Finding the prime factorization for these two numbers looks like a bit of a pain. However, if we let $a = 144$ and $b = 270$, we know that

$$\gcd(a,b) = \gcd(a, b - k \cdot a) = \gcd(144, 270 - 144) = \gcd(144, 126) = \gcd(126, 144).$$

We have reduced the complexity of this problem. Again, we can take $a = 126$ and $b = 144$. Notice how we always let b, the second number, be the larger of the two numbers (the order of a and b in $\gcd(a,b)$ does not matter). We have

$$\gcd(126, 144) = \gcd(126, 144 - 126) = \gcd(126, 18) = \gcd(18, 126).$$

Wow, this seems to be working really well! Let's try that again!

$$\gcd(18, 126) = \gcd(18, 126 - 7 \cdot 18) = \gcd(18, 0).$$

At this point, it is clear that $\gcd(18, 0) = 18$. Therefore, $\gcd(144, 270) = \boxed{18}$ as well. $\quad\square$

This last example showed us how to use our recently discovered gcd trick to evaluate $\gcd(a,b)$ for some integers a and b. We will define this process, called the **Euclidean Algorithm** generally as follows:

If we are trying to find $\gcd(a,b)$, rearrange these two numbers so that the second number b is the larger of our two numbers. Now, perform the following four steps:

- If $a = 0$ or $b = 0$, then the final answer is the nonzero number. In this case, we are done.

- If $a \neq 0$ and $b \neq 0$, then consider the number $b - k \cdot a$, where $0 \leq b - k \cdot a \leq a$ and k is an integer. This number is somewhere between 0 and a, which means that we have reduced the complexity of the problem. Replace the current value of b with this number and proceed.

- Switch the order of a and b so that the second number in $\gcd(b, a)$, or a, is greater than the first number, or b.

- Switch the names of a and b to make sure that b is always the second number in the pair. Namely, so that we have $\gcd(a, b)$.

Problem 103

Find the $\gcd(100, 144)$.

Proof. Like the last problem, we will set $a = 100$, and $b = 144$, so we know that

$$\gcd(a, b) = \gcd(a, b - k \cdot a)$$

or

$$\gcd(100, 144 - 100) = \gcd(100, 44) = \gcd(44, 100)$$

Now that we have reduced the complexity of this problem, we can take $a = 44$ and $b = 100$. We let the second number be the larger number (the order of a and b in $\gcd(a, b)$ does not matter). Now, we have

$$\gcd(44, 100) = \gcd(44, 100 - 44) = \gcd(44, 56).$$

Now that this method is working, let's keep going.

$$\gcd(44, 56) = \gcd(44, 56 - 44) = \gcd(44, 12) = \gcd(12, 44)$$

Keep going, we get

$$\gcd(12, 44) = \gcd(12, 44 - (3 \cdot 12)) - \gcd(8, 12)$$

. Next, we get

$$\gcd(8, 12) = \gcd(8, 12 - 8) = \gcd(4, 8)$$

After this, we get

$$\gcd(4, 8) = \gcd(4, 8 - (4 \cdot 2)) = \gcd(0, 4)$$

At this point, it is clear that $\gcd(0, 4) = 4$. Therefore $\gcd(100, 144) = \boxed{4}$. $\qquad\square$

Problem 104

Find the $\gcd(36, 56)$.

Proof. In this problem, we can set $a = 56$ and $b = 36$, so this means that since

$$\gcd(a, b) = \gcd(a, b - a),$$

we have

$$\gcd(36, 56) = \gcd(36, 56 - 36) = \gcd(36, 20) = \gcd(20, 36)$$

Now that we have reduced the number, we will keep doing this until we get our answer. Next, we will get

$$\gcd(20, 36) = \gcd(20, 36 - 20) = \gcd(20, 16) = \gcd(16, 20)$$

Next, we will get

$$\gcd(16, 20) = \gcd(16, 20 - 16) = \gcd(16, 4) = \gcd(4, 16)$$

Repeating this step, we get

$$\gcd(4, 16) = \gcd(4, 16 - 4) = \gcd(4, 12)$$

Doing this again, we get

$$\gcd(4, 12) = \gcd(4, 12 - 3 \cdot 4) = \gcd(0, 4)$$

At this point, it is clear that $\gcd(0, 4) = 4$. Therefore $\gcd(36, 56) = \boxed{4}$. $\square$

Problem 105
Find the $\gcd(50, 100)$.

Proof. We will start the problem by setting $a = 50$ and $b = 100$. Now, we will solve the problem and get

$$\gcd(a, b) = \gcd(a, b - k)$$

or

$$\gcd(50, 100) = \gcd(50, 100 - 50) = \gcd(50, 50)$$

After doing the same step again, we get:

$$\gcd(50, 50) = \gcd(50, 50 - 50) = \gcd(50, 0) = \gcd(0, 50)$$

At this point, it is clear that $\gcd(0, 50) = 50$. Therefore $\gcd(50, 100) = \boxed{50}$. $\square$

§20.1 Euclidean Algorithm Practice Problems

Problem 106

Use the Euclidean Algorithm to find gcd(100, 200).

Problem 107

Use the Euclidean Algorithm to find gcd(130, 190).

Problem 108

Use the Euclidean Algorithm to find gcd(56, 84).

Part IV
Algebra in the AMC 8

§21 Introduction

Algebra is the study of variables and how numbers relate to one another. As opposed to Number Theory, algebra focuses on all numbers, including complex numbers.

§22 Sequences and Series

In this section, we will be uncovering what the difference a series and sequence is, as well as how to solve them.

> **Problem 109**
>
> In the arithmetic sequence $5, 10, 15, \cdots$ find the next five terms.

Proof. In this problem, given a sequence, we have to find the next terms. Because this sequence has a simple, it is relatively simple to find the pattern. The pattern for this sequence is that every consecutive number is 5 greater than the previous number. That means that the next 5 terms would be $\boxed{20, 25, 30, 35, 40, 45}$. □

> **Problem 110**
>
> In the sequence, $1, 1, 2, 3, \cdots$ find the next 5 terms.

Proof. In this sequence, it is clear that there is not a constant by which each consecutive number increases by. This means that there is a different pattern. Looking at the sequence, we notice that every number is equal to sum of the previous two numbers. For example, 2 is the sum of $1 + 1$. 3 is the sum of $2 + 1$, and so on. This sequence is very special in math and is known as the Fibonacci series.

Now that we have the pattern, we can find the next 5 numbers. Using the pattern, we can deduce that the next 5 numbers of the sequence is $\boxed{5, 8, 13, 21, 34}$. □

After solving some problems related to sequences, we can now find what a series is. The difference between a sequence and series is that a sequence is a particular order of certain numbers creating a pattern. A series on the other hand is the sum of the numbers in a sequence. Now that we know the difference, let's solve some problems related to series'.

Problem 111

Find the series of 5, 10, 15, 20.

Proof. When solving a series, you have to add up all the numbers. If the sequence is short, adding up the numbers will be easy, but if it is long and the numbers are large, it will take too much time. Too make it easier, we have an equation. The equation is $S = \frac{A1+Af}{2} \cdot n$. S, is the sum of all the terms, $A1$ in this equation is the first term, Af is the final term and n is the number of terms in the sequence.

Now, all we have to do is substitute the corresponding values into the equation. $A1$ will be 5, Af will be 20 and n will be 4. This gives the equation $S = \frac{5+20}{2} \cdot 4$. Solving this equation, we get that the series of this sequence is $\boxed{50}$. We can check by adding up the numbers in the sequence. Doing so, we get 50, proving our answer to be correct. $\square$

Problem 112

Given the partial sequence: 3, 6, 9,..., find $A4$, $A5$, and $A6$. Using these terms, find the sum of this sequence.

Proof. Before we start to solve for the sum, we have to find the 4th, 5th, and 6th terms. To do this, we need to find a pattern. Looking at the first 3 numbers, we notice that each consecutive number increases by 3. Using this pattern, we can apply this to find the next 3 numbers. We can find that $\boxed{A4 = 12, A5 = 15, \text{and} A6 = 18}$. Now that we have the first and the last term, we can substitute it into the equation to find the sum. Once we substitute it, we get the equation, $S = \frac{3+18}{2} \cdot 6$. Solving this equation, we get the answer for the series as $\boxed{63}$. $\square$

Up until now, all the sequences and series were all arithmetic meaning that they grew at a constant rate. Now, let's look at geometric sequences and series. Geometric sequences grow at an exponential rate. Now, let's look at a problem.

Problem 113

Given geometric sequence: 2, 4, 8..., find the next 3 terms.

Proof. In this problem, each term grows exponentially by a certain power. Remember that the way we found out the difference between two terms in an arithmetic sequence was to subtract a term by its previous one. In a geometric sequence, we divide a term by its previous to find the constant. Now, if we divide $\frac{4}{2}$, we get that the constant is 2. This means that each term in the sequence is two times larger than its previous term.

Now that we know the constant, we can use it to find the next 3 terms. So, if we multiply each previous term by 2, we get that the 3rd term or $\boxed{A3 = 16}$, then the 4th term or $\boxed{A4 = 32}$, and finally the 5th term of $\boxed{A5 = 64}$. $\qquad\square$

Problem 114

Find the sum of the geometric sequence: 3, 9, 27, 81, 243.

Proof. When solving for the sum of a geometric sequence, we have a different equation than from an arithmetic sequence. The equation or a geometric sequence is $S = \frac{a \cdot (r^n - 1)}{(r-1)}$, where a is the first term, r is the constant or common ratio, n is the number of terms and S is the sum.

Now that we know what each term means, we can then plug in the appropriate values for each. If we plug in the values, we get $S = \frac{3 \cdot (3^5 - 1)}{3-1}$. If we solve this equation, we get that the S value or the sum for this geometric sequence is $\boxed{363}$. $\qquad\square$

Problem 115

Find the sum of the geometric sequence: 2, 4, 8, 16, 32, 64.

Proof. In this problem, we will solve it the same way as the last one. We have the equation $S = \frac{a \cdot (r^n - 1)}{r-1}$, which we can plug the appropriate values into. Plugging in the values, we get $S = \frac{2 \cdot (2^6 - 1)}{(2-1)}$. Now, if we solve this equation, we get that the sum for this sequence is $\boxed{126}$. $\qquad\square$

Now that we have a feel for general sequences, let's look at arithmetic and geometric sequences in more detail.

§22.1 Arithmetic Sequences and Series

An arithmetic sequence is in the form $a, a + d, a + 2d, \cdots, a + d(n-1)$, where $a + d(n-1)$ is the nth term of the sequence. The term a is the first term of an arithmetic sequence, and d is called the common difference. In arithmetic sequences, we add the common difference to get to the next term.

Problem 116

The second term of an arithmetic sequence is 5, and the fourth term is 11. Then, what is the sixth term?

Proof. **Solution 1:** We know that the second term is of the form $a + d$ because we only have to add the common difference once to get from the first term to the second term. Similarly, the fourth term has the form $a + 3d$ because we have to add the common difference 3 times to get from the first term to the fourth term. We know from the given information that $a + d = 5$ and $a + 3d = 11$. We can solve the system of equations (which we will later learn how to do) to get $a = 2$ and $d = 3$. Then, the sixth term is of the form $a + 5d$ and we can solve for it with the values of a and d to get $a + 5d = 2 + 5 \cdot 3 = \boxed{17}$.

Solution 2: In order to get from the second term to the fourth term, we must add twice the common difference. To get from the fourth term to the sixth term, we must again add the common difference twice. Twice the common difference is just the difference of the second term and the fourth term, or $11 - 5 = 6$. We can add this to the fourth term to get the sixth term, which is $11 + 6 = \boxed{17}$. $\qquad \square$

> **Remark 22.1.** Don't just blindly apply formulas! Think about what you are doing. It could become a whole lot easier.

Let's see the sum of an arithmetic sequence.

Theorem 22.2 (Sum of an Arithmetic Sequence)

We can prove that the sum of the terms in an arithmetic sequence is just the average of the first and last terms multiplied by the number of terms in the sequence.

Let's try an example.

Problem 117

What is the sum of the terms of the arithmetic sequence that starts at 4, ends at 192, and has 20 terms?

Proof. Due to our last theorem, we don't need to find all of the terms in the sequence. We just need the average of the first and last terms and the number of terms. Well, we are given all of the things we need, so let's just compute! We get that the average of the first and last terms are $\frac{4 + 192}{2} = 98$. When we multiply this by the number of terms, we get $98 \cdot 20 = \boxed{1960}$. $\qquad \square$

If we do not know the number of terms, we can just use the $a + (n - 1)d$ form of the terms in an arithmetic sequence.

Problem 118

How many terms are in the sequence that starts with 6 and ends in 151 with common difference 5?

Proof. The first term has the form a. The last term has the form $a + (n-1)d$, where n is the number of terms in the sequence. If we subtract the forms of these two, we get $a + (n-1)d - a = (n-1)d = 5n - 5$, where we used the fact that $d = 5$ in the last step. So, we have that $151 - 6 = 5n - 5$. Solving this (as we will later learn) gives us $n = \boxed{30}$. $\square$

§22.2 Geometric Sequences and Series

A geometric sequence is in the form $a, ar, ar^2, ar^3, ar^4, \cdots, ar^{n-1}$, where ar^{n-1} is the nth term of the geometric sequence. Again, a is the first term of the sequence, and r is called the common ratio. In geometric sequences, we multiply by the common ratio in order to get to the next term.

Problem 119

The second term of a geometric sequence is 4, and the fourth term is 16. Then, what is the sixth term?

Proof. This is the exact same as the first problem in the last section, except it is now geometric instead of arithmetic. Let's use the smart way this time. To go from the fourth term to the sixth term, we must multiply by the common ratio twice, which is the same as what we must do to get from the fourth term to the sixth term. So, we can just multiply the fourth term 16 by $\frac{16}{4} = 4$ to get $16 \cdot 4 = \boxed{64}$. $\square$

Let's see the sum of a geometric sequence.

Theorem 22.3 (Sum of a Geometric Sequence)

If the first term of a geometric sequence is a and the last term is ar^{n-1}, then the sum of a geometric sequence is $\frac{ar^n - a}{r-1}$. Note that n is the number of terms in the sequence.

Problem 120

What is the sum of the geometric sequence with first term 2, last term 486, and 6 terms in total?

Proof. Since the sixth term is of the form ar^5 and the first term is of the form a, we can divide $\frac{486}{2}$ to get r^5. We have $r^5 = 243$, or $r = 3$. Then, the common ratio is 3. We can use the formula from above to find the answer. We have $\frac{1458-2}{3-1} = \boxed{728}$. $\qquad\square$

§22.3 Sequences and Series Practice Problems

Problem 121

Find the sum of the arithmetic series: 15, 21, 27, 33, 39, 45.

Problem 122

Find the sum of the arithmetic series: 60, 120, 180, 240, 300.

Problem 123

Find the sum of the geometric series: 4, 16, 64, 4096, 16385.

§23 Introduction to Complex Numbers and the Argand Plane

Complex numbers are a very important part of math. They are very useful in quantum physics and mapping the motion of water or light waves. Complex numbers are typically written in the form of $a + bi$, where a is a and b are real numbers and $i = \sqrt{-1}$. Remember how we said in the beginning that i is imaginary. Therefore, a is said to be the "real part" and b is said to be the imaginary part (because it is multiplied by i, which is imaginary). In this section, we will be looking at a simple introduction to Complex Numbers (and imaginary ones!). Now, lets solve some problems related to complex numbers.

Problem 124

Solve for z: $z^2 + 25 = 0$.

Proof. In all equations in which we solve for a variable, we must first isolate the variable. Here, we isolate z^2 first. We get $z^2 = -25$. Taking the square root of both sides (and remembering to add our $\pm$ sign because we need both square roots), we get $z = \pm\sqrt{-25}$. We don't quite know how to deal with this, but we know that we can use the fact that $\sqrt{ab} = \sqrt{a} \cdot \sqrt{b}$. So, $\sqrt{-25} = \sqrt{-1 \cdot 25} = \sqrt{-1} \cdot \sqrt{25}$. We know that $\sqrt{25}$ is 5, but what about $\sqrt{-1}$? Well, we defined $\sqrt{-1}$ to be equal to i! So, adding the $\pm$ sign to get both square roots, we get $\boxed{\pm 5i}$. $\qquad\square$

Adding complex numbers is very intuitive, as we will now see.

Theorem 23.1 (Adding Complex Numbers)

We can add two complex numbers $a + bi$ and $c + di$ by adding their real and imaginary parts. Doing so, we get $(a + c) + (b + d)i$.

This makes sense because we cannot simplify the addition of a real number and a complex number. Let's try an example of this.

Problem 125

Compute : $(5 + 23i) - (4 + 3i)$.

Proof. We don't know about subtraction yet, but we do know that $-(4 + 3i) = -4 - 3i$. Then, we can rewrite the desired expression as $(5 + 23i) + (-4 - 3i) = \boxed{1 + 20i}$. $\qquad\square$

Theorem 23.2 (Multiplying Complex Numbers)

We can multiply complex numbers $a + bi$ and $c + di$ using the distributive property and the fact that $i = \sqrt{-1}$. The get

$$(a+bi)(c+di) = a(c+di)+bi(c+di) = ac+adi+bci+bd(i\cdot i) = ac+i(ad+bc)-bd = (ac-bd)+(ad+bc)i.$$

Let's try another example.

Problem 126

What is $(9 + 3i)(-5 - 3i)$?

Proof. Using the formula (which we can easily derive when doing this problem as well using the distributive property), we get $(-45 - (-9)) + (-27 - 15)i = \boxed{-36 - 42i}$. $\qquad\square$

Now, let's see an interesting attribute of complex numbers.

Problem 127

What is i^4? Then, what is i^{4n} for some n? What about i^{4n+1}, i^{4n+2}, and i^{4n+3}?

Proof. Since $i^2 = -1$, we have that $i^4 = (i^2)^2 = (-1)^2 = \boxed{1}$. Therefore, $i^{4n} = (i^4)^n = 1^n = \boxed{1}$. Then, $i^{4n+1} = i^{4n} \cdot i^1 = 1 \cdot i = \boxed{i}$. Similarly, we have that $i^{4n+2} = i^{4n} \cdot i^2 = 1 \cdot (-1) = \boxed{-1}$ and $i^{4n+3} = i^{4n} \cdot i^3 = 1 \cdot (-i) = \boxed{-i}$. Therefore, we know that $i^0 = 1, i^1 = i, i^2 = -1, i^3 = -i, i^4 = 1, i^5 = i, i^6 = -1, \cdots$. So, the powers of i repeat every 4 powers! $\qquad\square$

Now, let's look at one aspect of complex number multiplication.

Problem 128

What is $(a + bi)(a - bi)$?

Proof. Using complex number multiplication, we get our answer to be $\boxed{a^2 + b^2}$. $\qquad\square$

But wait a minute... Both a and b are real, so isn't $a^2 + b^2$ real as well? Well, it's no coincidence.

Theorem 23.3 (Conjugate of a Complex Number)

The conjugate of complex number $a + bi$ is $a - bi$. The product of a complex number and its conjugate is always real. If $z = a + bi$, then we denote the conjugate of z as $\bar{z}$.

Problem 129

What is $\frac{z+\bar{z}}{2}$? What about $\frac{z-\bar{z}}{2}$?

Proof. We have $z+\bar{z} = a+bi+a-bi = 2a$. So, $\frac{z+\bar{z}}{2} = \boxed{a}$. Similarly, $z-\bar{z} = a+bi-a+bi = 2bi$. So, $\frac{z-\bar{z}}{2} = \boxed{bi}$. Therefore, $\frac{z+\bar{z}}{2}$ is the real part of z, and $\frac{z-\bar{z}}{2}$ is the imaginary part of z. $\quad\square$

Now, let's look at complex denominators.

Problem 130

Write $\frac{2-i}{3+2i}$ as a fraction with a real denominator. Use this to write the fraction in the form $a + bi$.

Proof. We know that $(3+2i)(3-2i)$ is real, since $3-2i$ is the conjugate of $3+2i$. Therefore, why don't we just multiply the numerator and denominator by $3-2i$? We get

$$\frac{2-i}{3+2i} \cdot \frac{3-2i}{3-2i} = \boxed{\frac{4-7i}{13}}.$$

We can separate out the fraction to get the desired form. We get $\boxed{\dfrac{4}{13} - \dfrac{7}{13} \cdot i}$.   □

Now, let's take a look at the Argand Plane, or the Complex Plane.

Example 23.4 (Argand Plane)

We can graph complex numbers on the Argand Plane. Complex numbers are used heavily in advanced geometry. Here, we learn how to plot them. The Argand Plane is similar to the Cartesian Plane, except the $x-$axis represents the real part of a complex number and the $y-$axis represents the imaginary part of a number. To elaborate, the point/number $a + bi$ can be plotted in the complex plane on the point corresponding to (a, b) in the Cartesian Plane.

We won't going too much into depth into complex numbers here, as they are not frequently required in the AMC 8.

§23.1 Introduction to Complex Numbers and the Argand Plane Problems

Problem 131

In this section, we used the conjugate of a complex number to make the denominator of a complex fraction real. Use the same method to bring $\frac{1}{a+bi}$ into the form $x + yi$. Try to do the same thing with $\frac{c+di}{a+bi}$.

Problem 132

Solve for z: $4z^2 + 12 = 0$.

Problem 133

In the Argand Plane, what is the distance from the origin to the point $z = a + bi$? How is this related to $z \cdot \bar{z}$? (Hint: Use the Pythagorean Theorem.)

Problem 134 (AHSME)

What is $(i - i^{-1})^{-1}$? (Hint: The term $a^{-1} = \frac{1}{a}$ for all a.)

§24 Introduction to Functions

Functions are a very powerful topic because it allows you to find out what number you get, if you plug it into a certain equation. Functions are used in a lot of higher level topics such as Calculus even though it might seem simple. Now, let's start by looking at a problem related to functions.

Problem 135

Given the function: $f(x) = \frac{x}{x^2+1}$, find $f(-1)$, $f(0)$, and $f(2)$.

Proof. In this problem, we are given a equation and we have two find the values asked for. For those who don't know that $f(-1)$ means, it might be a bit hard. When they ask for $f(-1)$, what they want to you to do is to substitute -1 wherever there is an x in the equation. If we do this, we write the given function as $f(-1) = \frac{-1}{((-1^2)+1)}$. Now, all we have to do is solve the equation. If we do this, we get that $f(-1) = \boxed{-\frac{1}{2}}$.

Now, we just have to do the same for the other two values. If we plug in $f(0)$ into the equation, we get the equation $f(0) = \frac{0}{(0^2+1)}$. Without having to do any math, we see that this will equal to $f(0) = \boxed{0}$, because the numerator has a zero in it. Next, if we plug in 2, we get the equation $f(2) = \frac{2}{(2^2)+1}$. If we solve this equation, we get that the value for

$f(2) = \boxed{\frac{2}{5}}$. □

Problem 136

Given the function: $r(x) = 2x + 1$, find $r(5)$ and $r(20)$.

Proof. When solving this problem, we will tackle it like the last one. To solve it, we will first plug 5 into the equation to get, $r(5) = 2(5) + 1$. If we solve this equation, we get that the answer is $r(5) = \boxed{11}$. Next, if we plug in 20 into the equation, we get the equation: $r(20) = 5(20) + 1$. Solving the gives us the answer for $r(20) = \boxed{101}$. □

Problem 137

Given the function $f(x) = x^2$, find $(f(x))^3$.

Proof. When solving this problem, the $f^3(x)$ might look a bit daunting but it is very simple. Another way you can write it is $(f(x)^3)$. Looking at, it isn't that bad. Now all we have to

78

do is place $f(x)$ with x^2. Now, we have the expression: $(x^2)^3$. If we simplify the equation, we get $\boxed{x^6}$. $\qquad\square$

Problem 138

Given the function: $r(x) = 2x$, find $(r(x))^3$.

Proof. Just like the last problem, $r^3(x)$ can be written as $(r(x)^3)$. Now, we can substitute $2x$ into the x in $(r(x)^3)$. This will give us the value $(2x)^3$ or $\boxed{8x^3}$. $\qquad\square$

Problem 139

Given the 2 functions: $f(x) = 6x$ and $g(x) = x^2$, what are $f \circ g$ and $g \circ f$?

Proof. When you first look at it, $f \circ g$ and $g \circ f$, it can look a bit complicated but in reality, it really isn't. When there is a "$\circ$", it means to put the second function in the first. So, you can rewrite $f \circ g$ as $f(g(x))$. Now, if we start with $f \circ g$, we have to plug in x^2 into every x value in $f(x)$. If we write this, we would get: $f(x^2) = \boxed{6x^2}$.

Now, moving onto $g \circ f$, we would get $g(6x) = (6x)^2$. If we solve this, we would get that $g \circ f = \boxed{36x^2}$. $\qquad\square$

Problem 140

Given the 2 functions: $f(x) = 6x^2$ and $g(x) = x^2$, what is $f \circ g$ and $g \circ f$.

Proof. Like the last problem, we know that $f \circ g$ means f of g, and $g \circ f$ means g of f. If we start with $f \circ g$, we can rewrite it as $f(g(x))$, so we can plug in x^2, into $f(x)$. This will give is $f(x^2) = 6(x^2)^2$. So $f \circ g = \boxed{6x^4}$.

Now, moving onto $g \circ f$. We can rewrite it as $g(f(x))$. Now, we can replace the $g(x)$, with $6x^2$. This will give us $g(6x^2) = (6x^2)^2$. This gives us the answer to $g \circ f = \boxed{36x^4}$. $\qquad\square$

§24.1 Introduction to Functions Practice Problems

Problem 141

Given the function: $f(x) = 6\sqrt{x} + x^2$, find $f(5)$.

Problem 142

Given the function: $f(x) = \frac{x}{6x+1}$, find $f^2(x)$.

Problem 143

Given the functions: $f(x) = 2x + 1$ and $g(x) = x^2$, find $f \circ g$ and $g \circ f$.

§25 Linear Equations

Linear equations is a kind of equation which is put into a form with variables and constants. These constants stand in front a variable as a parameter. An example of a linear equation is $y = \frac{1}{2}x + 1$.

Problem 144

Solve the equation $3x + 11 = 5$.

Proof. This equation is very simple. For the first step, because we want to get the x by itself, we will first subtract 11 from both sides. When we do this, we get $3x = -6$. Now that we have $3x$ on it's own, we have to divide by 3 on both sides to get just x. When we do this, we get that $x = \boxed{-2}$. □

Problem 145

Solve the equation $6x - 3 = 3x + 14$.

Proof. Like the last problem, the first step is to get x by itself. To do that first, we will add 3 to both sides. This way, we have isolated the variable x, on one side, giving us the new equation: $6x = 3x + 17$. Now, the next step is to move the $3x$, on the right to the left. To do this, we will subtract both sides by $3x$. Now, we have the equation: $3x = 17$. Now that we have $3x$ on its own, we can divide both sides by 3 to just have x. Now, we our answer of $x = \boxed{\dfrac{17}{3}}$. □

Problem 146

Solve the equation $8x + 12 = x - 2$.

Proof. For the first step, we will need to subtract both sides by 12. This way, we will isolate the $8x$ by itself. Once we do this, we get the new equation: $8x = x - 14$. Next, we will subtract the x on the right to isolate the x on one side. To do this, we will subtract both sides by x, giving us the equation $7x = -14$. Now, for the final step, we need to divide both sides by 7 giving us the answer of $x = \boxed{-2}$. □

Problem 147

Solve the equation $15x - 30 = 8x + 56$.

Proof. The first step will be to isolate x. To do that, we will add 30 to both sides. This will give us the equation of $15x = 8x + 86$. Next, we will subtract $8x$ from both sides to isolate the x, giving is the equation: $7x = 86$. For the final step, we divide both sides by 7 giving us the answer of $x = \boxed{\dfrac{86}{7}}$ or $\boxed{12.28}$. □

§25.1 Linear Equations Practice Problems

Problem 148

Solve the equation: $\frac{3}{4}x + \frac{1}{2} = 3x + 1$ for x.

Problem 149

Solve the equation: $\frac{5}{3}x - \frac{2}{3} = 15x - \frac{1}{2}$ for x.

Problem 150

Solve for z: $\frac{z+3i}{z-3} = 2$. (Hint: Use both your complex numbers knowledge and your linear equations tools.)

§26 Systems of Equations

So far, we have solved equations with only a single variable, but now, we will solve equations with 2 variables. These equations will made of two equations to find the two variables. Before we start, we need to learn a way to solve the system of equations. To do that, we have three methods.

When trying to solve this system of equations, there are multiple ways to solve it. There are three main methods. The first is called **substitution**. Like the name says, we need to take one of the two variables and isolate it. This way, we can then substitute that value into the other equation. We can then solve for one variable and use it to solve for the other.

The second way to solve a system of equation, is called **elimination**. Elimination is the most complicated of the methods, but it can be used the most often. The way to use this method is set up in multiple steps.

- Of the two variables, choose one.

- Then, taking into account the constant in front, you need to make it so that both of the constants are matching. (You can do this by multiplying either equations by a certain number).

- Now, you will cancel out the variables in both equations by adding or subtracting them.

- This will leave only one variable remaining, which can be used to solve for the other one.

The next method is called **direct substitution**. We can use this method when both equations have a variable isolated on on side. Because there is the same variable in both sides of the equation, we can assume that the values on the other sides of the equations are also equal. So, we can set them equal to each other.

The final is **graphing**. This method is the least used because it involves graphing both lines and figuring out where the two lines intersect. Now, let's look at the problems

---

Problem 151

Solve the system of equations:

$x = 2y$;

$x + 2y = 8$

Proof. Now that we know all the methods, we can utilize them to solve the equations. If we look at the first equation, we see that the x is isolated on one side with the y on the other side. This means we can use the substitution method. If we take the value of x and substitute it into the other equation, we will only have one variable.

We can substitute $2y$ into the x in the second equation giving us the equation: $2y + 2y = 8$. If we simplify the equation, we get: $4y = 8$. If we solve for y, we get that $y = 2$. Now, we will need to substitute the y value back into the first equation. This will give is that the value of x is $x = 4$. Now, he way we write the answer for a system of equations an ordered pair. An ordered pair is written as (x, y), so we can write the answer as $\boxed{(4, 2)}$. $\qquad\square$

Problem 152

Solve the system of equations:
$x + 2y = 6$;
$2x + y = 3$

Proof. Unlike the last equation, we do not have a isolated variable in one of the equation. This means that in this problem, we cannot use substitution, so we will use elimination. Like the method states, we will first take a variable which in our case will be x. Like the name states, we will need to eliminate the x variable from both equations. To do this, we will need the same x constant in both equations.

To do this, we will need to get the first variable, which has a constant of 1, to a constant of 2. To do this, we can multiply the whole first equation by 2. This will give us a new equation of: $2x + 4y = 12$. Now, if we take the equation:
$2x + 4y = 12$
$2x + y = 3$.
Now, we can subtract both equations from each other to get rid of the xs. Now, we have one common equation with only y. The equation is $3y = 9$. This gives us that the value for $y = 3$. We can take this and substitute it back into the original first equation. This will give us that $x = 1.5$. We can rewrite as an ordered pair, giving us the answer of $\boxed{(1.5, 3)}$. $\qquad\square$

Problem 153

Solve the system of equations:
$y = 3x + 10$
$y = 2x - 1$

Proof. This problem is a classic example of direct substitution. We have one variable isolated in both equations. This means that we can set both of them equal to each other. If we set them equal to each other, we get one equation of $3x + 10 = 2x - 1$. If we simplify the equation by solving for x, we get the the equation: $x = -11$. Now, we can plug this back in to solve for y, giving us that $y = -22$. Now, can express the answer as an ordered pair and get: $\boxed{(-11, -22)}$. $\qquad\square$

§27 Introduction to Polynomials

A polynomial is an expression consisting of a variable and coefficients which are added, subtracted, multiplied or divided. Also, the powers in a polynomial are always integers. Now, let's look at some problems:

Problem 154

Given the polynomial: $x+1$, find the degree, the leading term, and the leading coefficient.

Proof. Before solving for each of the questions, let's look at what the questions is asking. The first part is to find the degree of the polynomial. The degree in a polynomial is the highest power on a variable. In this case, because there is only one variable, its power will be the highest. This gives us that the highest power of the polynomial is $\boxed{1}$.

Moving onto the next part. The next part asks you to find the leading term. The leading term is a combination of the leading variable as well as its coefficient. Looking at our polynomial, the only variable is $'x$ and its coefficient is 1. This means that the leading terms of this polynomial is $\boxed{x}$.

Lastly, lets look at the leading coefficient. Like the name says, we want to find the value that is front of leading variable. Because the leading variable in the polynomial is x, the leading coefficient of this polynomial will be $\boxed{1}$. □

Problem 155

Given the polynomial: $5x^2 + 2x + 3$, find the degree, the leading term, and the leading coefficient.

Proof. Let's tackle this problem like the last one. First, we need to find the highest power. To do this, let's look at the variables. Clearly, $5x^2$ has a power of 2 which is higher than $2x$, which means that the highest power of this polynomial is $\boxed{2}$.

For the next part, we need to find the leading term. The leading term in this polynomial is $\boxed{5x^2}$.

Now, to find the leading coefficient, we need to look at the leading term. the coefficient in front of the leading term is $\boxed{5}$. □

Problem 156

Given the polynomial: $3x^2 + 8x^5 + 2x + 3$, find the degree, the leading term, and the leading coefficient.

Proof. In this problem, the highest power does not belong to the first term, but rather the second one. The first term is $3x^2$ which has a power of 2, while the second term is $8x^5$, which has a power of 5. This means that the highest power in the polynomial is $\boxed{5}$.

When solving for the leading term in a polynomial, it is important that the term with the highest power is the leading term. If not, we have to arrange the terms to make it so. Now, after rearranging the terms, we get a new polynomial of $8x^5 + 3x^2 + 2x + 3$. Now, we get that the leading term for this polynomial is $\boxed{8x^5}$.

Now, moving on, we see that the leading coefficient of this polynomial is $\boxed{8}$. $\square$

Problem 157

Given the polynomial: $16^2x + 9x^5x + 36^9x + 16x + 3$, find the highest degree, the leading term, and the leading coefficient.

Proof. Just like the last problem, the highest power is not the first term. Taking that into consideration, if wee look through all the terms, we find that the term with the highest power is the term 36^9x. This means that this polynomial's highest power is $\boxed{9}$.

Now that we have to find the first term. Before we do this, because the first term in this polynomial is not the one with the highest power, we will need to reorder the polynomial. Once we reorder the polynomial, we get $36^9x + 9^5x + 16^2x + 16 + 3$. Now that we have reordered the polynomial, we can now find the first term. We find that the first term of this polynomial is $\boxed{36^9x}$.

Finally, we need to find the leading coefficient. To do this, we just need to look at the leading term. If we look at it, the constant in front of it is the leading coefficient. Now, looking at the term 36^9x, we can deduce that the leading coefficient of this polynomial is $\boxed{36}$. $\square$

§28 Quadratics

All equations are used to graph some sort of shape. For example, a linear equation is used to graph a line. A quadratic equation is used to graph a curve. One of the most common uses of a quadratic equation in real life is the arc of a ball. When you through a ball, it doesn't go straight forever, it forms a arc. This arc can be expressed as a quadratic equation. The standard form of a quadratic is: $ax^2 + bx + c$. Lets look at our first problem.

> **Problem 158**
>
> Factor the quadratic: $x^2 + 5x + 6$.

Proof. We will first start by factoring quadratics. How do we factor quadratics. Like every number has its own divisors, a quadratic has its divisors which are linear factors. For example, if we took the quadratic equation: $x^2 + 5x + 6$, we can split it up into $(x+2)(x+3)$. Now, how did we get this.

When solving quadratic equations, it can be bit difficult at first, but there is always a way to solve it. To factor a quadratic, the first step is to take the the c value, in this case is 6, and find its factors. The factors of 6, are: 1, 2, 3, 6. Now, we look to see which two numbers when added up, give is the middle number, in this case 5. As you can see, $2 \cdot 3$ is 6, while $2 + 3 = 5$. This means that these will be part of our factors. When writing the factors for a quadratic equation, we write as the product of linear factors. This means that we need to write 2 ad 3 as linear factors. The general way to write it would be in the form: $(x + r)(x + s)$, where r and s, are the two divisors. This means we can write it as $\boxed{(x+3)(x+2)}$ □

Let's practice factoring quadratics with another problem.

> **Problem 159**
>
> Factor the quadratic: $x^2 + 4x + 4$.

Proof. Just like the way we factor a quadratic is to find the factors of c. c, in this case is 4. The factors of 4 are: 1, 2, 2, 4. Out of these four factors, we need to find which two numbers equal to the middle value or b, which in this case is 4. The two factors are 2, and 2. Now, we need to write this as a product of two linear factors, which can be written as $\boxed{(x+2)(x+2)}$. □

Now that you know how to find the factors, you should know how to convert from factored form back into the equation in the form, $ax^2 + bx + c$.

> **Problem 160**
>
> Convert $(x+2)(x+3)$ back into a quadratic equation.

Proof. The first step is to us the distributive property. We first have to multiply the first term, in the first factor, by the first term in the second factor. This gives us $x \cdot x$ or x^2.

Then, we take the first term in the first factor and multiply it by the second term in the second factor. This gives us $3x$. Then, we have to take the second term in the first factor and multiply it by the first term in the second factor. This gives us $2x$. Finally, we take the second term in the first factor, and multiply it by the second term in the second factor. This gives us 6.

Now, we take all the terms and add them together. We have x^2, $3x$, $2x$ and 6. If we add them together, we get $\boxed{x^2 + 5x + 6}$. $\square$

Problem 161

Convert $(2x + 3)(2x + 1)$ into a quadratic equation.

Proof. Like the last problem, we will use the distributive property. First, we multiply $2x \cdot 2x$. This will give us $4x^2$. Then, we multiply $2x \cdot 1$, giving us $2x$. Next, we multiply $3 \cdot 2x$, giving us 6x. Finally, we multiply $3 \cdot 1$, giving us 3. This gives us the values $4x^2$, $2x$, $6x$ and 3. If we add all of them, we get the equation: $\boxed{4x^2 + 8x + 3}$. $\square$

So far, all the values of a, or the constant in front of the variable with a power greater than 1, has always been 1. Now, let's look at some problems which have an a value greater than 1.

Problem 162

Factor the quadratic: $4x^2 + 4x + 1$.

Proof. Just like the last few problems, to factor the quadratic, we will need to factor the c value, but the only difference is that we will also need to factor the a value. This is because up until now, the a value has been 1, so that meant that the the constants in front of x in the linear factors were also 1. Now that we have an a value that is greater than 1, the constants in front of x in the linear factors will also be greater than 1.

Now, lets factor. We can factor the 4 into: 1, 2, 2, 4; and the 1 into: 1 and 1. Now, we need to find the the two a value factors and the c value factor, which when multiplied, give us the on the middle value. As you can see, if take a 2 and multiply it by 1, we get 2. Because there are 2, 2s, we need to do this again giving us another 2. If we add them up, get 4 which is equal to the b value. This shows us that the factors are $\boxed{(2x + 1)(2x + 1)}$. $\square$

Problem 163

Factor the quadratic: $4x^2 + 8x + 3$.

Proof. Just like the last problem, we will factor the a value as well as the c value. If we factor the a value, we get that the factors are: 1, 2, 2, 4. And factoring the c value, gives us factors of 1 and 3. Now, to find the linear factors.

When trying to find the linear factors, we need to multiply the matching factors of a with the matching factors of c. In a, 1 matches 4 and, 2 matches 2. If we multiply $2 \cdot 3$, we get 6. Then if we multiply $2 \cdot 1$, we get 1. Adding 6 and 2 gives 8 which is the b value. Now, we know that the linear factors of this quadratic is: $\boxed{(2x + 3)(2x + 1)}$. $\quad\square$

Problem 164

Solve the quadratic equation: $x^2 + 5x + 6$.

Proof. Now that we know how to factor quadratics, we can use it to solve for a quadratic. Let's take our first example. The quadratic equation was: $x^2 + 5x + 6$. We factored it into $(x + 3)(x + 2)$. When solving a quadratic equation, the first step is to factor. Because we already did that, lets move onto the next step. We take the factored form and set it equal to 0. This gives the equation: $(x + 3)(x + 2) = 0$.

What does it mean when a product of two variables or numbers equals to 0. It means that one of them or both of the numbers have to equal to 0. We can take this principle and apply it to this problem as well. Because either $(x + 3)$or $(x + 2)$ has to equal to 0, we can separate them into two equations both linear factors. This ways makes it so that that either variable is equal to 0. If we take the first linear factor, we get the equation $x + 3 = 0$, giving us the answer of $x + 2 = 0$. This will give us that the answer for this quadratic equation is $\boxed{x = 3}$ or $\boxed{x = 2}$. $\quad\square$

Problem 165

Solve the quadratic equation: $4x^2 + 4x + 1$.

Proof. We know that the factors of this quadratic equation is: $(2x + 1)(2x + 1)$. Using this, we can solve the quadratic equation. If we set the factors equal to 0, we get the equation: $(2x + 1)(2x + 1) = 0$. Because both or either of the factors has to equal to 0, we can set the factors equal to 0. We will get the equation: $2x + 1 = 0$, because both factors are the same. If we solve this, we get the answer of $\boxed{x = -\dfrac{1}{2}}$. $\qquad\square$

§29 Vieta's Formulas

The Vieta's Formulas give us a nice relationship between a polynomial's roots and the coefficients. Here, we will be focusing on Vieta's Formulas with respect to quadratics.

Problem 166

Expand $(x + r)(x + s)$. How is this related to the quadratic form $x^2 + bx + c$? What are the roots of the quadratic represented by $(x + r)(x + s)$?

Proof. We start by multiplying out $(x + r)(x + s)$. We get

$$(x + r)(x + s) = x(x + s) + r(x + s) = x^2 + xs + rx + rs = \boxed{x^2 + (r + s)x + rs}.$$

We see that when we set this to the quadratic form $ax^2 + bx + c$, we get

$$x^2 + (r + s)x + rs = x^2 + bx + c.$$

We can then set the coefficients of the two sides equal to each other. We get

- $b = r + s$;

- $c = rs$.

Ok, but what does this really mean? To find out, we answer the third question in the problem.

To find the roots of $(x + r)(x + s)$, we can set $(x + r)(x + s) = 0$. From the zero product property, we find that at least one of $x + r$ and $x + s$ must be 0. The equation $x + r = 0$ gives $x = -r$ while the equation $x + s = 0$ gives $x = -s$. This means that $-r, -s$ are the two roots of the given quadratic.

Going back to the results we found earlier, $b = r + s$ and $c = rs$, **we see that b is the negative of the sum of the roots of the quadratic (Why?). We also see that $c = rs = (-r)(-s)$ is the product of the roots of the quadratic.** $\qquad\square$

Unsurprisingly, Vieta's formulas are helpful in finding the roots of a polynomial. Let's see how we can use it to find the roots of a quadratic.

> **Problem 167**
>
> Find the roots of $x^2 + 7x + 12$.

Proof. We present two solutions:

Solution 1 If our roots are r, s, then by Vieta's formulas, we must have that $-(r + s) = 7$ (the negative of the sum of the roots) and that $rs = 12$ (the product of the roots). So, we must find two numbers r, s such that

- $r + s = -7$;

- $rs = 12$.

With some trial and error (going through the factors of 12 perhaps), we find that $r, s = -3, -4$ works. Therefore, $\boxed{-3, -4}$ are the roots of this quadratic.

Solution 2 We know that factoring is a very simple way to find the roots of a quadratic. So, suppose our quadratic factors into $(x + r)(x + s)$. Then we have that

$$x^2 + 7x + 12 = (x + r)(x + s) = x^2 + (r + s)x + rs.$$

Note that the roots of this quadratic are

- $r + s = 7$;

- $rs = 12$.

From this, we can find that $r, s = 3, 4$. So, the negative of these is our answer. We get our answer to be $\boxed{-3, -4}$. □

> **Remark 29.1.** Don't get too attached to formulas! If you do, you will not be able to generalize your skills to solve new problems.

We can extend Vieta's formulas to quadratics that do not have a leading coefficient of 1.

> **Problem 168**
>
> Expand $(px + r)(qx + s)$. How does this relate to the quadratic form $ax^2 + bx + c$? What are the roots of $(px + r)(qx + s)$?

Proof. The expansion is easy as long as we use the distributive property.

$$(px+r)(qx+s) = px(qx+s)+r(qx+s) = pqx^2+psx+qrx+rs = \boxed{pqx^2 + (ps + rq)x + rs}.$$

Setting this equal to the quadratic form. we get

$$ax^2 + bx + c = pqx^2 + (ps + rq)x + rs.$$

Setting the coefficients equal, we find

- $a = pq$;

- $b = ps + rq$;

- $c = rs$.

This general formula can also be used to find the roots of a quadratic. First, we would factor the quadratic, leaving us with $(px + r)(qx + s)$. Then, we find the roots by setting each factor equal to 0. The equation $px + r = 0$ gives us $x = -\frac{r}{p}$ while the equation $qx + s = 0$ gives us $x = -\frac{s}{q}$. So the roots of this quadratic are $\boxed{-\dfrac{r}{p}, -\dfrac{s}{q}}$. $\square$

As you can imagine, this second method also helps us in finding the roots of polynomials.

Problem 169

Find the roots of $3x^2 + 7x + 2$.

Proof. We first need to find two numbers that multiply to get 2 and two numbers that multiply to get 3. Then we need to combine these factors somehow (through taking some pairwise product and adding them) to get 7. We find that since $2, 3$ are prime, the only two integers that multiply to get 2 are $2 \cdot 1 = 2$. Similarly, the only two integers that multiply to get 3 are $3 \cdot 1 = 3$. So, we must have our factored form be in the form

$$(3x + r)(x + s),$$

where $r, s = 1, 2$, but not necessarily in that order. We can try each combination, and we find that

$$\boxed{(3x + 1)(x + 2)}$$

is the correct combination. When we expand this, we get

$$(3x + 1)(x + 2) = 3x^2 + 7x + 12,$$

as desired. $\square$

§30 Rationalizing the Denominator

In this section, we will learn how to rationalize the denominator of a fraction. As the name implies, we do this when we have an irrational denominator in order to make the denominator rational. We generally do this because it is not very easy to work with irrational denominators.

> **Problem 170**
>
> Rationalize the denominator: $\frac{2}{\sqrt{5}}$.

Proof. First thing's first: Can we evaluate it? Um, no. Try using a calculator; it's not pretty.

To manipulate a fraction, we can multiply or divide both the numerator and the denominator by some number and we will get a different form of the same fraction. Make sure you understand that this is because this is the same as multiplying or dividing by 1. If we multiply the numerator and the denominator by $\sqrt{5}$, we get

$$\frac{2}{\sqrt{5}} \cdot \frac{\sqrt{5}}{\sqrt{5}} = \frac{2\sqrt{5}}{\sqrt{5} \cdot \sqrt{5}} = \boxed{\frac{2\sqrt{5}}{5}}.$$

But there's one question: How did we know to multiply the top and bottom by $\sqrt{5}$? Well, as we can see, it did the job because we get a rational number when we do $\sqrt{5} \cdot \sqrt{5} = 5$. Therefore, we *rationalize* the denominator. This will be the pattern in all rationalizing denominator problems. $\qquad\square$

> **Problem 171**
>
> Rationalize the denominator: $\frac{4}{2-\sqrt{3}}$.

Proof. We are dealing with a square root. We want a way to square 3. Unfortunately, multiplying by $2 - \sqrt{3}$ won't work this time. Try it and see. You will still get irrationals in the denominator. However, we also have another relation that helps us to square the individual components of a sum. This is the sum of squares. Specifically, we have that

$$(a + b)(a - b) = a^2 - b^2.$$

But how does this help us? Given the sum (or difference) of two numbers, we can multiply by the difference (or sum) of the two numbers to get the difference of squares of the two numbers.

If we apply this to our problem, we will get the difference of the squares of the two numbers, on of which will become rational as it is currently a square root. Specifically, we can do

$$\frac{4}{2-\sqrt{3}} \cdot \frac{2+\sqrt{3}}{2+\sqrt{3}} = \frac{8+4\sqrt{3}}{2^2 - \sqrt{3}^2} = \frac{8+4\sqrt{3}}{4-3} = \frac{8+4\sqrt{3}}{1} = \boxed{8+4\sqrt{3}}$$

$\square$

§31 Linear Inequalities

Like linear equations, linear inequalities are linear expressions but instead of an equal sign, the mediator is either a greater than, or less than sign. Now, let's look at some problems:

Problem 172

Solve the inequality: $3x + 6 < 0$

Proof. Just like linear equations, we need to solve the inequality for x, by isolating it. First, we need to subtract 6 from both sides. This way, we get the inequality, $3x < -6$. Now, we just have to subtract 3 on both sides and we get the answer: $\boxed{x < -2}$. $\square$

Problem 173

Solve the inequality: $6x + 16 < 3x + 3$

Proof. The first step in solving this problem is to first isolate the xs. To do this, we will first need to subtract $3x$ from both sides. After doing this, we get the inequality $3x + 16 < 3$. Now, we will need to subtract 16 from both sides giving us the inequality $3x < -13$. For the final step, we will need to divide both sides by 3 giving is the answer, $\boxed{x < -\frac{13}{3}}$. $\square$

Problem 174

Solve the inequality: $\frac{1}{2}x + \frac{3}{4} \geq \frac{3}{2}x - \frac{1}{2}$.

Proof. To solve this equation, we must first isolate the x. To do this, we will subtract $\frac{1}{2}x$ from both sides. This will give is the equation, $\frac{3}{4} \geq x - \frac{1}{2}$. For the next step, we will need to add $\frac{1}{2}$ to both sides. By doing this, we get the inequality $\frac{5}{4} \geq x$. If we reorder the inequality, we get the answer $\boxed{x \leq \frac{5}{4}}$. $\square$

§32 Quadratic inequalities

Quadratic inequalities like linear inequalities involve a less than or greater than sign, but having a linear expression, they a quadratic expression. Now, lets solve some problems.

Problem 175

Solve the inequality: $x^2 - x - 6 \geq 0$.

Proof. First, we will need to factor the quadratic. Like we learned in the last class, if we factor the quadratic, we get the inequality $(x-3)(x+2) \geq 0$. After this, we will need to solve the inequality. Before we start this, we have to consider the sign that will be shown the the inequality is split. To judge this, we look at the sign on the original inequality. With this, we can deduce that the sing for the split inequalities will also be $\geq$. Now, if we solve for both of the inequalities, we get $x-3 \geq 0$ or $x \geq 3$, and $x+2 \geq 0$ or $x \geq -2$.

Now given the two inequalities $x \geq 3$ and $x \geq -2$, how do we combine two. If we combine the two to get an answer, we get that the answer for the quadratic inequality is $\boxed{x \leq -2}$ and $\boxed{x \geq 3}$. $\qquad\square$

Problem 176

Solve the inequality: $(x+2)(x+4) < 0$

Proof. Unlike the last problem, the quadratic is already factored. So, we can now split the inequality. Now, because the sign is $<$. If we split up the inequality, we get the two separate inequalities $x+2 < 0$ and $x+4 < 0$. If we solve both of the inequalities, we get $x < -2$ and $x < -4$. Now, we have to combine the two inequalities. Unlike the last problem, the way to combine an inequality with the signs $<$ or $\leq$, is through a compound inequality. This means that when we combine the two, we get $\boxed{-4 < x < -2}$. $\qquad\square$

§33 Graphing Equations and Inequalities

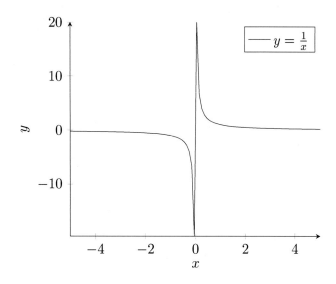

In this section, we will learn the basics of plotting in the Cartesian Plane. The **Cartesian Plane** is a tool used to graphically represent functions. We draw two perpendicular lines and label one as the **x axis** and one as the **y axis**. The x axis is plotted horizontally, while the y axis is plotted vertically. An example of the Cartesian Plane is above. We have plotted an advanced function $y = \frac{1}{x}$. An example of a general Cartesian Plane would be the following:

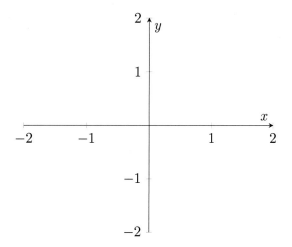

As you can see, these perpendicular lines (the x axis and the y axis) are actually just number lines. Let us try some simpler linear examples to get started.

We have been covering linear equations for some time know. Take the linear equation $y = x$. In order to plot this equation, we first make a table. In order to fill out this table, we will choose some x values and use the rule that $x = y$ to compute the corresponding y values. After this, we will plot these "points." But first, we need that table. Here's one:

x	y

Now, we need to fill this table out. In order to do that, we choose some x values that we want to compute the y values of. Let's take a nice range (not too large) of x values $-2, -1, 0, 1, 2$. Note that these were arbitrary choices, and in practice you may have to change these values. Our table becomes:

x	y
-2	
-1	
0	
1	
2	

So, now we find the corresponding y values. We do this by using the rule (given to us usually) that $y = x$. This means that every y value is just equal to its corresponding x value. For example, if $x = -1$, then $y = -1$ as well. We can fill the table out in this way to get:

x	y
-2	-2
-1	-1
0	0
1	1
2	2

Great! We have our table, so now what? We originally set out to plot the equation $y = x$. Now, we have a few points that represent this function. We can plot these points on the Cartesian Plane. For example, say we wanted to plot the first point in our table where $(x, y) = (-2, -2)$. We would first line up the point with -2 on the x axis (the first -2), and then we would line up the point with -2 on the y axis (the second -2). The point we would get is shown as follows:

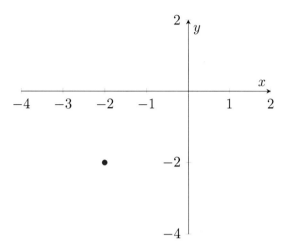

That's great! Now, all we have to do is plot the rest of the points, namely $(-1, -1), (0, 0), (1, 1), (2, 2)$. We get:

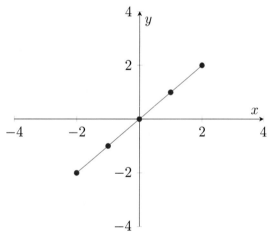

We connect these points with a line above because it turns out that if we use more than just the x values we did, we would get this line. We will prove this in the next problem. To elaborate, we would get this line if we had plotted over smaller and smaller intervals such as $x = -2, -1.9, -1.8, -1.7, \ldots, 1.8, 1.9.2$ or $x = -2, -1.99, -1.98, -1.97, \ldots, 1.98, 1.99.2$. If we continue to make these intervals smaller, we will end up with the above line.

Now that we have some intuition on graphing lines, let us try to prove the following:

Problem 177

Prove that the graph of the linear equation in the form $y = x$ is a line.

Proof. First, we think about the definition of a line. A line maintains constant direction and goes on forever. We know that last part is true for the graph of $y = x$, but what about the direction? Using simple trigonometry, we can prove (we won't do it here) that this is the same as saying that in the Cartesian Plane: any two points on the "line" must have a constant ratio between the difference of their y coordinates and their x coordinates. In other words, if we have two points

$$(x_1, y_1) \ (x_2, y_2),$$

then the ratio

$$\frac{y_2 - y_1}{x_2 - x_1}$$

must be constant.

In order to prove that this is the case for the equation $y = x$, we examine what happens when we take two points on this graph. Let our two points again be

$$(x_1, y_1) \ (x_2, y_2).$$

Then, by the rule $y = x$, we know that $y_1 = x_1$ and that $y_2 = x_2$. Then, we calculate the ratio

$$\frac{y_2 - y_1}{x_2 - x_1}$$

after substituting these values. We get

$$\frac{y_2 - y_1}{x_2 - x_1} = \frac{x_2 - x_1}{x_2 - x_1} = 1.$$

This **is** a constant! Now, we know that our equation $y = x$ is a line. $\square$

Here is the final graph of the line $y = x$:

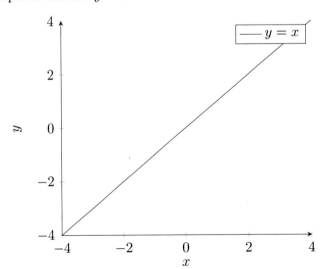

Note that this line goes forever in both directions.

Remark 33.1. This perhaps mystic ratio is called the **slope** of the line. The slope of a line determines how steep it is. A large slope corresponds to a steep line while a small slope corresponds to a flatter line.

A large positive slope corresponds to a line that goes from bottom left to top right and is close to being vertical. Here is the graph that corresponds to the equation $y = 10x$ (you can find this in the exact same way as we did with $y = x$):

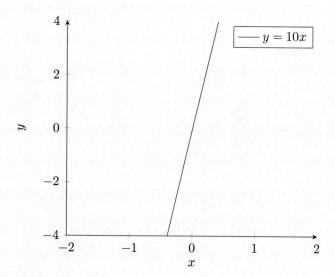

A small positive slope corresponds to a line that goes from bottom left to top right and is close to being flat. Here is the graph that corresponds to the equation $y = \frac{1}{10}x$:

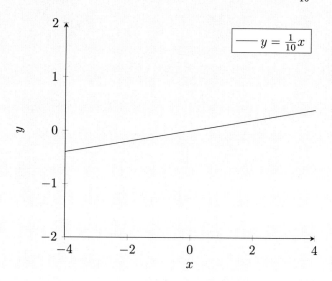

A slope of 0 corresponds to a flat line. Here is the graph of the equation $y = 0x$ or $y = 0$:

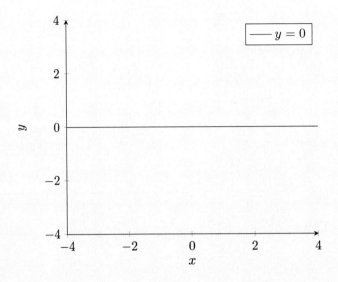

A large negative slope corresponds to a line that goes from top left to bottom right and is close to being vertical. Here is the graph that corresponds to the equation $y = -10x$:

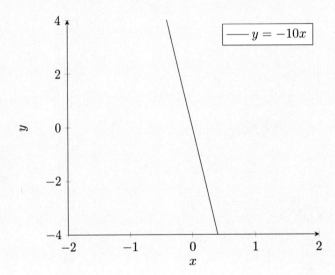

A small negative slope corresponds to a line that goes from top left to bottom right and is close to being flat. Here is the graph that corresponds to the equation $y = -\frac{1}{10}x$:

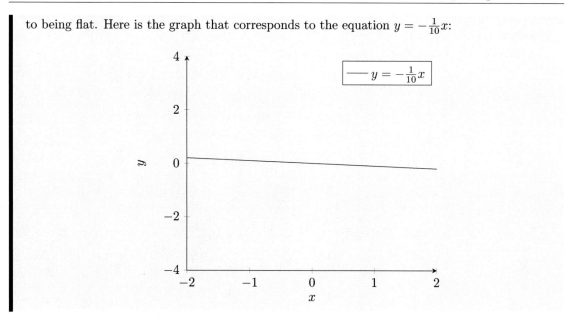

§34 Transforming Graphs

we learned how to graph $y = x$ and a few other lines in the form $y = mx$. Notice that these all go through the origin. What if we did not want the graphs to go through the origin, but to instead go through some other point? In this section, we will take about transforming graphs, and we will apply this technique to graphing more advanced linear equations.

Problem 178 (Basic Transformations)

Consider the following graph of $y = f(X)$:

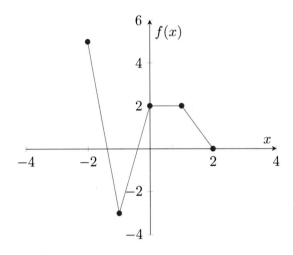

Find the graphs of

- $f(x) + 5$;
- $5f(x)$;
- $f(x + 5)$;
- $f(5x)$.

Proof. We first note that the original set $f(x)$ is the set of y coordinates for the points shown. This means that the values corresponding to $f(x) + 5$ are just y coordinates that are 5 more in value than the original set of points. This means that every point must be moved up by 5 units, or **translated up 5 units**. The corresponding graph to this would be

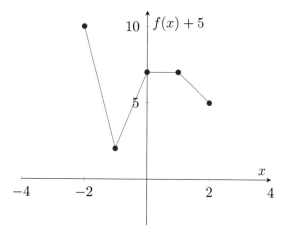

If you don't see how we moved this graph, make sure to look at the tick marks on the x axis and y axis.

For the graph of $5f(x)$, we note that we are now multiplying each y coordinate by 5, or **scaling the graph with respect to the x axis by a factor of** 5. This is the corresponding graph:

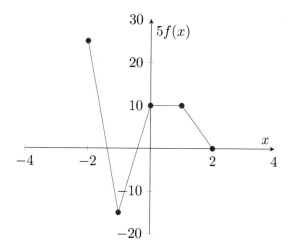

Again, make sure to notice the tick marks on the axes.

Now, we move onto the graph of $f(x+5)$. In this example, if we are plotting the point with x value x_1, then we are taking the y coordinate corresponding to the point which is 5 more than x_1, or $x_1 + 5$. This means that we are plotting the y coordinate of the point which is 5 units to the right onto this point (think about it!). Essentially, this means that we are **translating the graph 5 units to the left**. Note that this is not a shift right; it is a shift left. This trivial detail causes many people to make mistakes on these types of problems. The corresponding graph of this translation is the following:

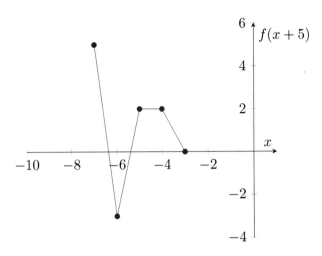

Finally, we turn to the graph of $f(5x)$. In essence, we are taking the x coordinate that is 5 times away from the y axis and plotting that y coordinate for the given x value (think about it!). This is just **scaling the graph down by a factor of 5 with respect to the y axis**. This is the resulting graph:

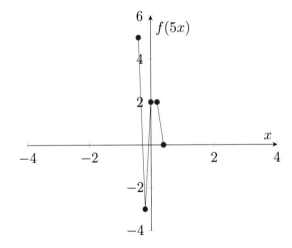

Hopefully, this last problem gave you some intuition on how graph transformations work. We will generalize these transformations in the next problem.

Problem 179

Say we graph the function $y = f(x)$. Describe the graphs of each of the following:

- $f(x) + c$;

- $c \cdot f(x)$;

- $f(x + c)$;

- $f(c \cdot x)$,

where c is positive. What if c is negative?

Proof. We break this problem up into two cases based on the value of c.

c **is positive** When c is positive, we have mostly the same thing as in the last problem. Check the last problem for the following results. The answers, in order, are:

- A c unit upward translation;

- A vertical scaling with respect to the x axis by a factor of c (note that this will be a shrink if $c < 1$);

- A c unit **leftward translation**;

- A horizontal scaling with respect to the y axis by a factor of $\frac{1}{c}$ (this will be a shrink if $c > 1$ and an enlargement if $c < 1$).

c **is negative** We tackle this one at a time. If c is negative, then **the graph of $f(x) + c$ is just a downward translation of the original graph by c units** (as opposed to an upward one).

What about $c \cdot f(x)$? We multiply each y coordinate by a negative number. This is actually just the same as multiplying by -1 and then by $-c$, a positive number (think about it!). When we multiply a y coordinate by -1, we just get its opposite! In other words, **we simply get its reflection over the x axis. After this, we scale the graph vertically by a factor of $-c$.**

Now, we move onto the graph of $f(x + c)$. It should not surprise you that this is now a rightward translation instead of a leftward translation. See if you can prove this the same way we did for when c was positive. This means that the graph of $f(x + c)$ is just a **rightward translation by c units** when c is negative.

Finally, we move onto $f(c \cdot x)$. Since c is negative, this is the same as multiplying the input by -1, or taking $f(-x)$ and scaling it horizontally by a factor of $-c$, a positive number (think about it!) with respect to the y axis. To get $f(-x)$, we take the y coordinate of the point with x value x_1 (for some x_1) and put that y value with the x value $-x_1$. In short, we essentially reflect each point of the graph across the y axis, thereby **reflecting the entire graph across the y axis. After doing this reflection, we then scale the graph horizontally by a factor of $-c$.** $\square$

This last problem was very important, as we will now see, and can be used in making more complex graphs, such as more complex linear functions.

Problem 180

Draw the graph of $y = f(x)$ where

$$f(x) = 3x + 5.$$

Proof. We have never seen this before, but we have seen its "parent function" which we will call $g(x) = x$. Note that this is the same as $y = x$. From here, we can do $3 \cdot g(x)$, from which we get:

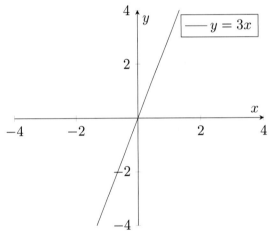

Now, we are one step closer to our answer because $3 \cdot g(x) = 3x = f(x) - 5$. Writing this compactly, we get $3 \cdot g(x) = f(x) - 5$, or $f(x) = 3 \cdot g(x) + 5$. So, we are trying to plot $3 \cdot g(x) + 5$. Remember, from the last problem this is just:

- A vertical scaling by a factor of 3 (we graphed this above);

- An upward translation by 5 units.

So, we get the graph:

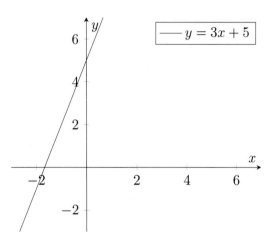

This is the final graph. □

It turns out that we can start with any generic linear equation (with variables x and y) and end up in the form presented in the problem. This form is (generically) $y = mx + b$. To graph this equation, we can start with $g(x) = y = x$ and manipulate our way to the answer.

§34.1 Graphing Systems of Equations

We mentioned earlier that we can solve systems of equations by graphing. In this section, we will do one such problem.

Problem 181

Solve the following system of equations by graphing:

$$y = 2x - 1$$

$$y = 3x - 2.$$

Proof. Both of these equations are graphs of lines. So, if we graph them, the solution(s) will be any point(s) (which will correspond to x and y values that satisfy the equations) at which the two graphs coincide. So, let's graph them!

The equation $y = 2x - 1$ is a vertical scaling by a factor of 2 and a horizontal translation by

1 unit of the graph $y = x$. Graphing this, we get:

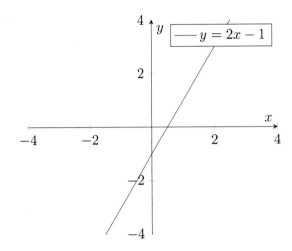

On the other hand, the graph of the equation $y = 3x - 2$ is given by a vertical scaling by a factor of 3 and a downward translation by 2 units of the graph $y = x$. The resulting graph is:

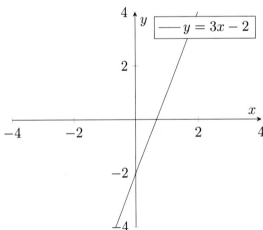

Putting these two on top of each other (and changing the color for clarity), we get:

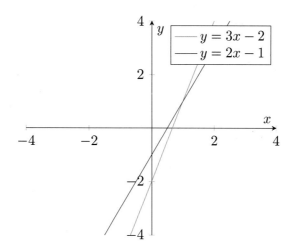

We see now (if we draw precisely enough) that the resulting graphs meet at the point $(1,1)$, which is our answer as explained above.

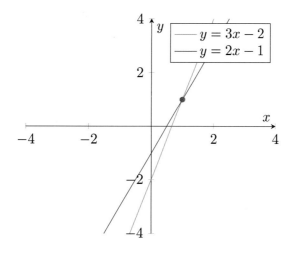

□

§35 Useful Expansions and Symmetric Sums

We have already covered how to solve and factor quadratic equations. Now, we will cover special cases in quadratic equations. These special cases are known as difference of squares, perfect squares, difference of cubes and sum of cubes. Before we start, lets look at the generic formula.

Problem 182

Prove that $(a+b)^2 = a^2 + 2ab + b^2$.

Proof. If we look at this problem, the way we can prove that is to expand $(a+b)^2$. We can rewrite $(a+b)^2$ as $(a+b)(a+b)$. Now, all that's left is to multiply it out. If we multiply the first term in the first factor by the second factor, we get $a^2 + ab$. Next, we take the second term in the first factor and multiply it out by the second term. By doing this, we get $ab + b^2$. Now, if we add up these two we get $a^2 + ab + ab + b^2 = \boxed{a^2 + 2ab + b^2}$. The same thing here applies to if there is a negative in between a and b. $\square$

Problem 183

Prove that $(a+b)(a-b) = a^2 - b^2$.

Proof. Just like the last proof, the way we can prove that those two expressions are equal is by multiplying the expression out. To start, if we multiply the first term in the first factor by the second term, we get $a^2 - ab$. Next, if we multiply the second term by the second factor, we get $ab - b^2$. Now, we just have to add them together. If we add them, we get the expression, $a^2 - ab + ab - b^2 = \boxed{a^2 - b^2}$. $\square$

Problem 184

Prove that $(a+b)(a^2 - ab + b^2) = a^3 + b^3$.

Proof. Once again, the only way to prove that these two are equal is two expand the expression. To start off, we have to multiply the first term in the first factor by the second factor. By doing this, we get $a^3 - a^2b + ab^2$. Then, we take the second term in the first factor and multiply it by the second factor. If we do this, we get $a^2b - ab^2 + b^3$. Now, all that we have to do is add these two together and we get the expression, $a^3 - a^2b + ab^2 + a^2b - ab^2 + b^3 = \boxed{a^3 + b^3}$. We use the same method if the sign in the final expression is negative. $\square$

Problem 185

Given the quadratic: $x^2 + 4x + 4$, factor the quadratic.

Proof. The generic form of a perfect square is written as $a^2 + 2ab + b^2$ or $a^2 - 2ab + b^2$. We can factor this to be $(a + b)^2$ or $(a - b)^2$.

We already know how to factor a quadratic. Our first step is to take the factor of the c term, which in this case is 4. The factors of 4 are (2 and 2), and (4 and 1). Now, we have the pairs of factors of 4. Looking at these two pairs, we can see that the pair, (2 and 2), satisfies the condition that if added give is the b value and if multiplied give is the c value. Now, if we write the factored form as the product of two linear factors, we get that the factored form is $(x + 2)(x + 2)$.

Now, this is not the most simplified form. When you multiply a variable or number by itself, you can write it as a square of that number. So, we can write, $(x + 2)(x + 2)$, as $\boxed{(x + 2)^2}$. $\qquad\square$

Problem 186

Given the factors, $(x - 8)(x + 8)$, multiply it out into quadratic form.

Proof. This is problem is an example of difference of squares. The generic form for the difference of squares is $(a - b)(a + b)$. If we multiply it out, we get the quadratic $a^2 - b^2$. This quadratic does not have a b term but does have an a and c. Now, let's go to our problem.

We have multiplied out factors before, and we do it the same way. The first step is to take the first term in the first factor and multiply it by the who second factor, to get $x \cdot (x + 8)$. This gives us $x^2 + 8x$. The next step is to take the second term in the first term and multiply it by the second factory, to get $-8 \cdot (x + 8)$. This gives us $-8x - 64$. Now, we have to take these two terms and add them together. If we add them, we get $x^2 + 8x - 8x - 64$. If we simplify this, we get the answer $\boxed{x^2 - 64}$. $\qquad\square$

Now, that we have covered difference of squares and perfect squares, we will move onto sum and difference of cubes.

Problem 187

Factor the difference of cubes: $a^3 - 27$.

Proof. This problem is a classic example of a difference of cubes. The generic form for a difference of cubes is, $a^3 - b^3$ or $a^3 + b^3$. If we factor it, we get the product, $(a - b)(a^2 + ab + b^2)$ or $(a + b)(a^2 - ab + b^2)$. Notice in the second factor that the b term rather having $2a$ as its constant like we know only has a.

Now, to factor the difference of cubes. The first factor in the generic form shows $a - b$. In this case the a, corresponds to a in our polynomial and the b corresponds to 3. Now, we can write the first factor as $(a - 3)$. Now, moving onto the second factor, because we have the a and b values, we can find that the second factor is $a^2 + 3 \cdot a + 3^2$, which if simplified is $a^2 + 3a + 9$. Now that we have the two factors, we can write the answer and get $\boxed{(a - 3)(a^2 + 3a + 9)}$. $\square$

Problem 188

Factor the sum of cubes: $c^3 + 8$.

Proof. This problem is very similar to the last problem, but the sign is different. This means that the generic formula is also different. In this case, the generic formula is $a^3 + b^3$, which if factored gives us $(a + b)(a^2 - ab + b^2)$.

If we factor the problem, we first get the a and b values which are c and 2 respectively. Now, for the first factor is $(c + 2)$. Notice how the sign is different than from the previous problem. Because the sign is different in the first problem, there will be slight variation in the second factor as well. In the second, using the generic formula, we get $c^2 - 2 \cdot c + 2^2$, which simplifies to $c^2 - 2c + 4$. Now, if we combine the two factors, we get the answer $\boxed{(c + 2)(c^2 - 2c + 4)}$. $\square$

§36 Rate Problems and More Proportions

Proportions are a very vest and commonly covered topic. In this section, we will just go over the basics.

Problem 189

5 apples 10 dollars, how much does 15 apples cost?

Proof. This problem is very simply, we are given the cost of 5 apples and we need to find the cost of 15 apples. The way to do this is to set up a proportion. A proportion compares two values of equal units. An example of a proportion would be $\frac{a}{b} = \frac{c}{d}$. In this example, a and c must have the same units and b and d must have the same units. Now, if we look at our problem we can set up a proportion with the given values.

If we set up a proportion, it would look like, $\frac{5}{10} = \frac{15}{d}$. Notice that 5 and 15 have the same units so they are in the same place on either side of the equation. Now, to solve for d, we need to cross multiply. If we cross multiply, we get the equation $5 \cdot d = 10 \cdot 15$. Now, if we solve for d, we get that 15 apples cost $\boxed{30}$. □

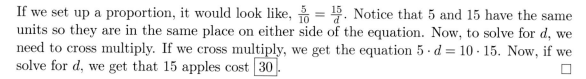

Problem 190

A ten foot pole casts an 8 foot shadow. How long is a pole which casts a 12 foot shadow?

Proof. Just like the last problem, we will need to set up a proportion. If we set a proportion based on the units, we get the equation, $\frac{pole}{shadow} = \frac{10}{8}$. Now, if we compare the $\frac{10}{8}$ to the 12 foot shadow, we can set up the equation, $\frac{10}{8} = \frac{x}{12}$. If we cross multiply, we get the equation, $x \cdot 8 = 12 \cdot 10$. If we solve for x, we get the the height of the pole to create a 12 foot shadow is $\boxed{15}$. □

Problem 191

It takes 3 days for 4 people to paint 5 houses. How long will it take 2 people to paint 6 houses?

Proof. To set up the equation of proportionality, we first need to confirm the units. If we set a proportionality with the units, we get $\frac{houses}{(people) \cdot (days)} = \frac{5}{12}$. Now, if we set up an equation with the given value, we would get $\frac{5}{12} = \frac{6}{(2) \cdot (days)}$. If we solve this equation for days, we get $days = \frac{12 \cdot 6}{5 \cdot 2}$. This gives that it takes $\boxed{\dfrac{36}{5}}$ days for 2 people to paint 6 houses. Notice how as the number of houses goes up, so does the amount needed to paint it. □

Problem 192

It is 4 o'clock now. How many minutes will pass before the minute and hour hands of the clock are coincident?

Proof. If we draw a picture of a clock with the minute and hour hand in their corresponding positions, we notice that it 20 minutes for the minute and hour to meet up right? Well this actually not right. This is because during the time that the minute hand moves, the hour hand is also moving. Because 20 is $\frac{1}{3}$ of 60 minutes of an hour, the hour hand would have moved $\frac{1}{3}$ of the way from3 to 4. This means that we have to take 20 minutes and add $\frac{1}{3}$ of the time between 3 and 4 in minutes which is 5 minutes. This means that we have to add $\frac{5}{3}$ onto 20. This gives that answer of $\boxed{\dfrac{240}{11}}$. □

113

§37 Linear Equation Word Problems

Word problems are just linear equations that are written as words. To solve the problems, we must interpret these words as a set of linear equations. When solving the problems, we will follow a three step procedure:

Step 1 Define all the variables.

Step 2 Write the equations described by the problem.

Step 3 Solve the equations.

Problem 193

Johnny is twice as old as Gina. Johnny is five years older than Gina. How old is Johnny?

Proof. This problem is a very classic problem related to age. Our first step is to define our variables: let Johnny's age be J and Gina's age be G. Second, we need to determine the equations. Since Johnny is twice as old as Gina, J must be twice G, so $J = 2G$. Because Johnny is five years older than Gina, then J must be 5 more than G, so $j = G + 5$. We now have a system of equations. We can use substitution to find that the $G = 5$. Now, if we substitute this value back into the first equation, we get that Johnny is $\boxed{10}$. $\square$

Problem 194

The units digit in a two digit number is three times the tens digit. If the digits are reversed, the resulting number is 54 more than the original number. Find the original number.

Proof. Our first step is to define the variables: let the tens digit be t and the units digit be u. The value of the number is then $10T + u$. Since the units digit is three times the tens digit, $u = 3t$. If the digits are reversed , the resulting number has value $10u + t$. So now, if we subtract the number reversed number from the original, it should give us 54. This will be set up as $10t + u - (10u + t) = 9u - 9t = 54$. We now have two equations, $u = 3t$ and $9u - 9t = 54$. The second equation if divided by 9 on both sides can be simplified to $u - t = 6$. If we use substitution to solve for the system of equations, then we get that $t = 3$. If we solve for u, we get $u = 9$. Now, if we combine the two digits, we get the number $\boxed{39}$. $\square$

114

Problem 195

Jim drives to his mother's house, which is 40 miles away, and then drives back. On the way there he drives back. On the way there he drives 40 miles an hour, but on the way back he drives 20 mph. What is his average speed for the whole trip?

Proof. You might think that to find the answer, we just take the average of the speeds which gives us 30 mph, but that is not how to solve the problem. When we solve this problem, we have to make use of the equation, $d = r \cdot t$, where d is the distance, r is the speed, and t is the time. If we want to find the average speed, we also have to look at the distance. The total distance for round trip is 40 + 40 or 80 miles. We have the parameter for distance but we now need to time to find the average speed. To do this, let's look at how long it takes to go in each direction. Because he goes 40 mph towards his mother's house, it will take him 1 hour, and because he is going 20 mph back, it will take him 2 hours. This is a 3 hour total round trip time. Now, that we have distance and time, we can solve for speed. If we plug this back into our equation, we get the equation, $80 = r \cdot 3$. Now, if we solve for r, we get that $\boxed{r = \dfrac{80}{3}}$ mph. $\qquad\square$

Problem 196

A frog swims 8 miles downstream in 2 hours. She returns in 14 hours. How fast does the frog swim in still water?

Proof. In this problem, we also have to make use of the equation, $d = r \cdot t$. When a frog swims downstream, because it goes with the current, we also have to add the speed of the current to the frogs speed in still water. Say the frogs speed in still water is x and the currents speed is y. We now have the speed of the frog when its going downstream, which is $x + y$, and its upstream speed is $x - y$, because its going against the current. Now, substitute the appropriate values into the equation and we get that equation for downstream is,

$$(x + y) \cdot (2) = 8$$

and upstream is,

$$(x - y) \cdot (14) = 8$$

Now, we have a system of equations, which if we solve, we get that x or the frog's speed in still water is $\boxed{\dfrac{16}{7}}$. $\qquad\square$

115

§38 Exponents and Logarithms

Exponents and logarithms are inverse functions. Like how a square and square root are inverse functions, the same apply to exponents and logarithms. Exponents are written in the form $a^b = c$. The inverse of that, logarithms, are written in the form $\log_a c = b$. Now, lets look at some problems.

Problem 197

Compute: 3^3

Proof. This is a very simple problem. It is asking what is the value if 3 is multiplied by itself 3 times. The way to solve this is to multiply it by itself 3 times. So we get $3 \cdot 3 \cdot 3$, which gives us $\boxed{27}$. $\square$

Problem 198

Compute: 2^8

Proof. Just like last problem, to solve the problem, we have to break down the exponent. 2^8 can be written as $2 \cdot 2 \cdot 2 \cdot 2 \cdot 2 \cdot 2 \cdot 2 \cdot 2$. Now, if we multiply it, we get $\boxed{256}$. $\square$

Problem 199

Compute: $9^{\frac{3}{2}}$

Proof. So far, we have been solving problems with only integer exponents. Now, our exponent is a fraction. The way we solve this is once again to break down our problem but in a different way. When ever we have a fractional problem, the way we break it down is to split the fraction exponent into a fraction times an integer. Now, if we do the same thing with our current problem, we get $9^{\frac{1}{2} \cdot 3}$.

Now that we have split it up, we see that we still have a fraction. The fraction when split up should always have a 1 as its numerator. Because we this, we can change it from $9^{\frac{1}{2} \cdot 3}$ to $(\sqrt{9})^3$. Whenever we have a power in a fraction, we take that and convert it from a fractional exponent to a root to the degree of the denominator. Because the denominator was 2, we get a square root. If our denominator was 3, we would get a cube root. Now, if we simplify the the square root, we get 3^3. Remember, when we took the square root, we left the 3 untouched so we have to take the square root of 9 to the power of 3. If we do this, we get the answer, $\boxed{27}$. $\square$

116

Problem 200

Compute: $\log_3 81$

Proof. To solve this, there is a very simple method. Because a logarithm is the inverse of a exponent, that means that we can convert a logarithm into an exponent. The way we convert a logarithm into an exponent is very simple. We take the base of the logarithm which in this case is 3 and take it to the power of the unknown, which we can name c and set that equal to the power of the base or in this case 81. If we do this, we get the equation $3^c = 81$.

Now, all that we have to do is solve for c. c represents the number of times that we have to multiply 3 by itself to get 81. We know that we have to multiply 3, 3 times to get 27. We also know that $27 \cdot 3 = 81$. This means that we have to multiply 3, 4 times to get 81, which can also be written as $3^4 = 81$. Now we know that $\log_3 81 = \boxed{4}$. $\qquad\square$

Problem 201

Compute: $\log_2 64$

Proof. We solve this problem the same way we did with the last one. To convert it to a fraction, we take the base which is 2, to the power of the unknown which in this case can be expressed as the variable c and set it equal to the power of the base which is 64. Now, we have the equation $2^c = 64$.

Now, to figure out what c is, we use powers of 2 that we already know. We know that $2^4 = 16$. We also know that $16 \cdot 4 = 64$. If we use this, we can say that $16 \cdot 4$ which can also be written as $16 \cdot 2 \cdot 2 = 64$. Now, all we need to do is add up the 2's. We have 4 from 16 and 2 from 4, which gives is that $2^6 = 64$. This gives us that, $\log_2 64 = \boxed{6}$. $\qquad\square$

Part V
Counting and Probability in the AMC 8

§39 Introduction

In this next unit, we will learn about two key concepts that are not only used in the AMC 8, but also in real life applications. These two concepts are Counting and Probability.

You might be thinking: "But I already know how to count!: 1, 2, 3, …." Well, yes, this is counting, but not all of it. Sometimes we don't simply wish to count things in order such as a set of objects. Rather, we often wish to count sets that are out of order or don't start from 1 or don't even increment by 1. For example, what is the number of numbers in the list $9, 10, 11, \ldots, 27$? This is not as obvious, even if you *are* able to find the answer.

Counting is one of the founding principles of Probability. In non-rigorous terms, Probability is the "chance" that something will happen. For example, the chance of you flipping a *heads* on a coin flip (with a fair coin) is $50\% = \frac{1}{2}$. At a high level, this is because you would expect that you would get heads once for every two times you flip the coin.

We will see problems like these as well as several others in the next few sections.

§40 Basic Counting

Problem 202

How many numbers are in the list: $1, 2, 3, \ldots, 24$?

Proof. There are $\boxed{24}$ numbers in this list.

We see this if we start counting from the first number onward. On the first number, we count "1" and the number in the list corresponding to the first number is 1. Then, we count the second number "2" in the list, which just so happens to be 2 as well. Going in this fashion, we find that we count the ith number "i" when we count the corresponding number in the list, which is also i (make sure you see why this is the case; the numbers are in a consecutive sequence starting from 1). We then find out answer to be 24. $\square$

Try proving the following yourself:

Remark 40.1. The number of numbers in the sequence

$$1, 2, 3, \ldots, n$$

is n.

Hopefully, this makes some intuitive sense. Let's see something slightly harder. We encountered this problem in the Introduction section.

Problem 203

What is the number of numbers in the list $9, 10, 11, \ldots, 27$?

Proof. We could do this several ways, which is why we present two possible solutions:

Solution 1 We can make this into a problem that we have seen before. We know that when counting the number of numbers in the set

$$1, 2, 3, \ldots, n$$

that there are exactly n numbers. So, what if this question could be made into a simpler problem like this one? Well, one way to do that would be to bring the first term down to 1. We could do this by subtracting 8 from every term. This would make the list

$$9 - 8, 10 - 8, 11 - 8, \ldots, 27 - 8$$

$$= 1, 2, 3, \ldots, 19.$$

By the last problem, it is easy to deduce that the number of numbers in this list is $\boxed{19}$.

Solution 2 We could also make this into a $1, 2, 3, \ldots, n$ counting problem by simply adding $1, 2, 3, \ldots, 8$ to the beginning to this set of numbers. Then, our set would become

$$1, 2, 3, \ldots, 7, 8, \ 9, 10, 11, \ldots, 27,$$

where the set in blue is what we wish to count and the set in red is the set that we have artificially added to make the problem easier. The whole set has 27 numbers while the artificial set has 8 numbers. To get our answer, we simply subtract these two to get $27 - 8 = 19$, which is the same answer as above. $\square$

> **Remark 40.2.** In solution 2 of the last problem, we used a technique where we **overcounted**, and then we subtracted the part of the set that we did not need, leaving us with the correct answer.
>
> In general, this technique of counting the wrong things, and then combining them to get the right thing, is called **complementary Counting**. We often do this when the thing that we wish to exclude from our answer is easier to count than the answer itself. complementary Counting is an extremely powerful fundamental part of Counting that also shows up in Probability.

Let's do an extension of the last problem:

Problem 204 (From a to b)

Assuming that $a \leq b$, how many numbers are in the list

$$a, a+1, a+2, \ldots, b-1, b?$$

Proof. We again present two solutions, just like in the last problem:

Solution 1   We can make this into a simpler one by transforming it into a list such as the following:

$$1, 2, 3, \ldots, n.$$

We can do this (as in the last problem) by simply subtracting $a - 1$ from every number in the original list. This is because we will then get

$$a - (a-1), a+1 - (a-1), a+2 - (a-1), \ldots, b-1-(a-1), b-(a-1)$$

$$= 1, 2, 3, \ldots, b-a, b-a+1.$$

As we have seen in the past, the number of numbers in the list

$$1, 2, 3, \ldots, n$$

is n. Therefore, the number of numbers in the list

$$1, 2, 3, \ldots, b-a, b-a+1$$

is $\boxed{b-a+1}$.

Solution 2   We can also attempt complementary counting here. To do this, we can append the list

$$1, 2, 3, \ldots, a-2, a-1$$

to the beginning of the desired list we wish to count the number of elements of. Therefore, our list becomes

$$1, 2, 3, \ldots, a-2, a-1, a, a+1, a+2, \ldots, b-1, b.$$

We wish to count the number of elements in the blue portion of the above list, but it's not very easy to do so. We can instead use complementary counting by first counting the number of blue **and** red elements combined and then subtracting the number of elements in the red portion. This should give us the number of elements in the blue portion, our desired answer.

The whole list is in the form

$$1, 2, 3, \ldots, n$$

so the number of elements in the list

$$1, 2, 3, \ldots, a-2, a-1, a, a+1, a+2, \ldots, b-1, b$$

is simply b. Additionally, the number of elements in the list

$$1, 2, 3, \ldots, a-2, a-1,$$

is $a = 1$. Therefore, the number of elements in the blue list is

$$\text{elements in whole list} - \text{elements in red list} = b - (a-1) = \boxed{b - a + 1}.$$

$\square$

Now, we will look at a slightly more complicated version of this counting.

Problem 205

How many elements are in the list

$$28, 32, 36, \ldots, 96, 100?$$

Proof. This is a slightly different problem than last time because now, instead of incrementing the numbers in our list by 1 every single time, we increment the elements by 4 every single time. Every number is in fact a multiple of 4. Specifically, 28 is the 7th multiple of 4, 32 is the 8th multiple, and so on until 100, which is the 25th multiple.

Aha! It seems as if the *multiple numbers* increment by 1 each time. We can see this more clearly if we just divide each element by 4. Then, we get the list

$$7, 8, 9 \ldots, 24, 25.$$

> **Remark 40.3.** Note that since we are only counting the **number of elements** and not the sum of the elements, or anything else that has to do with the actual **value** of the elements, we can change the elements themselves as long as we do not remove any of the elements.

Note that this list has the same number of elements as the initial list we started with. We simply divided every number by 4, which does not change the **number of elements in the list**. Make sure you see why we can do this.

Now, it is very easy to count the number of numbers in the list

$$7, 8, 9 \ldots, 24, 25.$$

The answer is simply (by the formula we found in the last problem) $25 - 7 + 1 = \boxed{19}$. $\square$

Now, we will look at a practical application of counting, where we count arrangements.

Problem 206

I have 3 shirts and 4 pants in my drawer. If I wish to choose 1 shirt and 1 pant to wear on some given day, how many outfits (shirt and pant combinations) could I possibly wear?

Proof. There are a few ways to do this, so we present 2 solutions:

Solution 1   We can start by labeling the 3 shirts: Shirt 1, Shirt 2, Shirt 3. We can also label the 4 pants Pant 1, Pant 2, Pant 3, Pant 4. Then, we can organize a table like the following:

	Shirt 1	Shirt 2	Shirt 3
Pant 1	Shirt 1, Pant 1	Shirt 2, Pant 1	Shirt 3, Pant 1
Pant 2	Shirt 1, Pant 2	Shirt 2, Pant 2	Shirt 3, Pant 2
Pant 3	Shirt 1, Pant 3	Shirt 2, Pant 3	Shirt 3, Pant 3

Make sure you see how we set up the table. We simply listed all of the possible combinations between 1 shirt and 1 pant.

We can count by hand that there are $\boxed{12}$ outfits.

Solution 2   It was excruciating to make that table and count all of the combinations! What if I had 10 shirts and 30 pants? I would never be able to fit that table onto paper! (Well, maybe, but not likely.) There has to be a better way to do this!

Let's think about it now. When I select an outfit, I first have to choose a shirt (it's basically the same thing if I choose a pant first). There are 3 ways to do this, of course, because I have 3 shirts. Then, I must choose a pant. I can do this in 4 ways because I have 4 pants. So, once I choose a shirt in 1 of any 3 ways, I can choose 1 pant out of 4 for each of those 3 shirts I chose before. Basically, I can choose 3 shirts, and then 4 pants **for each of those 3 shirts**. Therefore, my answer is $3 \cdot 4 = \boxed{12}$ outfits. If you do not understand how this works, make sure to look at the above table to see how it relates to this solution. Also make sure you understand this solution, as it will make counting so much easier.   □

§40.1 Basic Counting Problems

Problem 207

How many numbers are in the list

$$1, 2, 3, \ldots, 12345?$$

Problem 208

How many numbers are in the list

$$12345, 12346, 12347, \ldots, 54321?$$

Problem 209

How many numbers are in the list

$$29, 33, 37, 41, \ldots, 101?$$

(Hint: This is very similar to a problem we did in this section.)

Problem 210

How many numbers are in the list

$$123, 133, 143, \ldots, 12345678909876543?$$

(Hint: What is the increment?)

Problem 211

I have 10 shirts and 30 pants. How many 1 shirt and 1 pant outfits can I possibly wear on a given day?

Problem 212

I am making a pizza! I can choose 1 of 3 types of breads, 1 of 5 types of cheeses, 1 of 10 fruits, and 1 of 20 vegetables. How many pizzas are possible? (Hint: There are 3 bread types to choose from. For every 1 bread type I choose, there are 5 cheeses I can choose. For every 1 bread and 1 cheese I choose, there are 10 fruits I can choose. Keep going with this argument!) (Note: This is why we don't use tables. Try making a table for this problem. Is it possible?)

§41 Factorial!

To get some intuition behind the concept of factorials, we do a problem:

Problem 213

How many ways are there to arrange 4 books on a shelf?

Proof. We start by placing the books on the shelf one by one. There are 4 books that we can choose for the first position on the shelf, 3 ways to choose the book in the second position, 2 ways to choose the book in the third position, and only 1 way to choose the book in the fourth position.

You might recognize this example as being similar to the Basic Counting section. We can multiply all of these options in order to get the total number of ways to arrange 4 books on a shelf.

Specifically, we can start by noting that for every book that we choose for the first position, there are 3 books that we can choose for the second option. Since there are 4 ways to choose the book in the first position, we have that there are $4 \cdot 3 = 12$ ways to choose the first 2 books. Then, for each one of the combinations we choose for the first 2 books, there are 2 options we have for the book in the third position. Since there are 12 ways to choose the first 2 books, there are $12 \cdot 2 = 24$ to choose the first 3 books. Finally, we see that for each of the first 3 books that we choose, there is only one option left to choose for the last book. Since there are 24 combinations for the first 3 books, there are $24 \cdot 1 = \boxed{24}$ ways to choose the orderings of all 4 books. □

You might have noticed that all we really did was $4 \cdot 3 \cdot 2 \cdot 1 = 24$ to get our answer, though the actual reasoning behind this was quite long.

In fact, this is true in general. You will be asked to prove as a practice problem that the number of ways to arrange n objects in a line (as we did in the last problem with arranging 4 books on a shelf) is

$$n \cdot (n-1) \cdot (n-2) \cdot \ldots \cdot 2 \cdot 1.$$

This should already make some sense to you. There are n options for the item in the first position in the line, $n-1$ options for the second, etc. until we have only 1 option for the last item. Then, we can multiply all of these to get the above formula.

This formula is so special that mathematicians have developed a notation for it.

Definition 41.1 (Factorial!) — By definition,

$$n! = n \cdot (n-1) \cdot (n-2) \cdot \ldots \cdot 2 \cdot 1.$$

So, the number of ways to arrange n objects in a line is $n!$. The number of ways to arrange 4 objects (or books) in a line (or on a shelf) is $4! = 4 \cdot 3 \cdot 2 \cdot 1 = 24$. Factorials are used in many places, including permutations and combinations.

125

Problem 214

Find the value of 3!.

Proof. We have that $3! = 3 \cdot 2 \cdot 1 = \boxed{6}$. □

Problem 215

Find the value of 6!.

Proof. Again, by definition, we have that $6! = 6 \cdot 5 \cdot 4 \cdot 3 \cdot 2 \cdot 1 = \boxed{720}$. □

Problem 216

Compute: $\frac{6!}{3!}$.

Proof. In this problem, we are given a fraction with factorials in the numerator and the denominator. The way we solve is to cancel the factorials out. So, we rewrite the numerator as a product such as $6! = 6 \cdot 5 \cdot 4 \cdot 3!$ (expand this and prove it to yourself!). Now, we can cancel the 3! in the numerator and the denominator, which gives

$$\frac{6 \cdot 5 \cdot 4 \cdot 3!}{3!} = \frac{6 \cdot 5 \cdot 4 \cdot \cancel{3!}}{\cancel{3!}} = 6 \cdot 5 \cdot 4 = \boxed{120}.$$

□

§41.1 Factorial! Problems

Problem 217

Compute: 4!.

Problem 218

Compute: $\frac{8!}{5!}$.

Problem 219

Compute: $\frac{15!}{9!}$.

126

Problem 220

There are 6 people in a row. How many ways are there to arrange them in that row?

Problem 221

How many ways are there to arrange a deck of cards? (No Jokers! This deck has 52 cards.) Write your answer in terms of a factorial.

Now, try computing your answer by hand. (Hint: Don't spend too much time on it! It's impossible! Use a calculator instead) ☺

Problem 222

How many ways are there to arrange 8 people in a line?

§42 Permutations

Let's start with a problem to introduce intuition.

Problem 223

I have 5 objects. In how many ways can I choose 3 objects from these to be in a line in any different order? (Every order of 3 objects is considered a different "way.")

Proof. Essentially, we can choose 3 objects out of 5 as long we do not end up with the same 3 objects in the same exact order.

So, we can start by considering how we make a line of 3 objects. We start by selecting the first object in the line. Similar to the Factorial! section, we can choose any of the 5 objects to sit in the first spot. Once we have done that, we have 4 options remaining for the second spot, since one spot is already full. Up till now, there are $5 \cdot 4 = 20$ ways to choose the first 2 objects in the line. In order to choose the third and final object for this line, we can choose any of the 3 remaining objects. Therefore, there are $20 \cdot 3 = \boxed{60}$ ways in total. □

So, the total computation we did was $5 \cdot 4 \cdot 3$. Notice how this is the exact same as $\frac{5!}{2!} = \frac{5!}{(5-3)!}$ and we wanted to choose 3 objects out of 5. Is this a coincidence?

Problem 224

I have n objects. In how many ways can I choose k of those objects to be in a line?

Proof. This is the same as the last problem, just with different numbers. We have n choices for the 1st object in the line, $n - 1$ choices for the 2nd object in the line, $n - 2$ choices for the 3rd object in line, and so on. In general, we have $n - i + 1$ choices for the ith object in the line (make sure you see why this is true!). So, we have $n - k + 1$ choices for the kth object in the line, or the last object. So, we can multiply these to get our answer. Our answer is

$$n \cdot (n - 1) \cdot (n - 2) \cdot \ldots \cdot (n - k + 1).$$

But we don't box this. We saw in the last problem that there might be a better way to represent this. Specifically, the sequence reminds us of factorials. This expression is actually almost equal to $n!$. However, it does not go all the way to 1. It is missing the $(n - k) \cdot (n - k - 1) \cdot (n - k - 2) \cdot \ldots \cdot 2 \cdot 1$ at the end in order for it to be $n!$ (make sure you see why this is true!). Hoping to simplify this using this factorial, we multiply our answer above by

$$\frac{(n - k) \cdot (n - k - 1) \cdot (n - k - 2) \cdot \ldots \cdot 2 \cdot 1}{(n - k) \cdot (n - k - 1) \cdot (n - k - 2) \cdot \ldots \cdot 2 \cdot 1}.$$

So, we get

$$n \cdot (n - 1) \cdot (n - 2) \cdot \ldots \cdot (n - k + 1) \cdot \frac{(n - k) \cdot (n - k - 1) \cdot (n - k - 2) \cdot \ldots \cdot 2 \cdot 1}{(n - k) \cdot (n - k - 1) \cdot (n - k - 2) \cdot \ldots \cdot 2 \cdot 1}$$

$$= \frac{n \cdot (n - 1) \cdot (n - 2) \cdot \ldots \cdot (n - k + 1) \cdot (n - k) \cdot (n - k - 1) \cdot (n - k - 2) \cdot \ldots \cdot 2 \cdot 1}{(n - k) \cdot (n - k - 1) \cdot (n - k - 2) \cdot \ldots \cdot 2 \cdot 1}.$$

The reason we do this is because now we can reduce the numerator to just $n!$, like so:

$$\frac{n!}{(n - k) \cdot (n - k - 1) \cdot (n - k - 2) \cdot \ldots \cdot 2 \cdot 1}.$$

Ok, that was nice. But wait! Look at the denominator! It's just $(n - k)!$, so we can reduce that as well. Our final answer is

$$\boxed{\frac{n!}{(n - k)!}}.$$

$\square$

When we count the number of possible ways to choose some items from a set of items in a certain order like in the last problem, we are doing **Permutations**. When we try to choose 3 objects out of 5, we are "permuting 3 objects from a set of 5 objects."

The standard form for a permutation is $_nP_k$. This is the same as asking the last problem: "I have n objects. In how many ways can I choose k of these objects to be in a line?" We can use the formula we found in the last problem to evaluate such problems. As a reminder, the equation that we use to solve for the number of permutations is, $_nP_k = \frac{n!}{(n-k)!}$.

Problem 225

Compute: $_6P_1$.

Proof. To solve this problem, we have to use the equation, $\frac{n!}{(n-k)!}$. We know that using the general form, $n = 6$ and $k = 1$. If we plug in the values of n and k, we can find out the number of combinations. By plugging in the values, we get, $\frac{(6)!}{(6-1)!}$. If we simplify this, we get, $\frac{6!}{5!}$. Now, once we get this, we can solve for the answer. But, before we do, do we really want solve for 6! and 5!. That will take too much time and effort so there is an easier way.

We can simplify the numerator(6!), into $6 \cdot 5!$. Now, we have a common factor in the numerator and the denominator. This gives us, $\frac{6 \cdot 5!}{5!}$, which can be simplified to get the answer $\boxed{6}$. □

Problem 226

Compute: $_8P_2$

Proof. Just like the last problem, the way we solve this problem is by using the equation, $\frac{n!}{(n-k)!}$. We know that $n = 8$ and $k = 2$. We can now substitute these values back into the equation. If we do this, we get, $\frac{(8)!}{(8-2)!}$. If we simplify this, we get, $\frac{8!}{6!}$. Once again, we are at the part where we split up the numerator so that the problem is easier to simplify. We can split up the numerator into, $8 \cdot 7 \cdot 6!$. Now, we have a common factor in both the denominator and the numerator. Now, we can solve for the answer to get, $\frac{8 \cdot 7 \cdot 6!}{6!}$. Now, we can cancel the 6! from both numerator and denominator, so we that we get a simplified form of $8 \cdot 7$. This brings to our answer of $\boxed{56}$. □

Problem 227

Given the word, *Binky*, find how many ways you can arrange the letters.

Proof. In this problem, we will need to use permutations to figure the number of arrangements. To find the number of arrangements, we use the equation, $\frac{n!}{\text{repetitions!}}$. In the equation, what "repetitions" means is if there are any letters in the word that are repeating, then we need to put the number of times they repeating factorial. Now, we will look at our problem. The value for n is 5, and there are no numbers that are repeating so we don't have any number in the denominator. This means that we get the equation, 5! or $\boxed{120}$. □

Problem 228

Given the word, *Butterfly*, find how many ways you can arrange the letters.

Proof. Just like the last problem, we will be using permutations to find out the number of arrangements that are possible. We will use the equation, $\frac{n!}{\text{repetitions}!}$. Using the equation, we know that $n = 9$, and we have a repetition. The letter t, appears twice so we have 2! in the denominator. If we plug it into the equation, we get, $\frac{9!}{2!}$. Just like we did in the first two problems, we can rewrite the numerator into $\frac{9 \cdot 8 \cdot 7 \cdot 6 \cdot 5 \cdot 4 \cdot 3 \cdot 2!}{2!}$. We can cancel out the 2!, and we are left with $9 \cdot 8 \cdot 7 \cdot 6 \cdot 5 \cdot 4 \cdot 3$, which if simplified, gives us $\boxed{181440}$.   □

§42.1 Permutations Problems

Problem 229

Compute: $_8P_6$.

Problem 230

Compute: $_{15}P_9$.

Problem 231

Given the word, *Mississippi*, find the number of ways you can arrange the letters.

§43 Combinations

Again, we start with a problem to gain intuition about this concept.

Problem 232

I have 5 objects. How many ways are there to choose 3 objects from these 5 objects? (We are not arranging these in a line, so it does not matter what order the 3 objects are in.)

Proof. This is like the last section except we are not choosing the objects in any particular order. We can start by computing the number of ways to choose 3 objects from 5 when order matters (or when we have to put them in a line). There are $\frac{5!}{(5-3)!} = \frac{5!}{2!} = 5 \cdot 4 \cdot 3 = 60$ ways to do this. However, we counted the different ways to *order* each of these sets of 3

130

objects that we choose. But we don't want that! Specifically, for each of the sets of 3 objects that we have, we counted all of the ways to order those 3 objects, which is exactly $3! = 6$. We counted each "set" 6 times. For each of these 6 duplicate sets, we only want 1 that represents the contents of this set of objects. Therefore, we can just divide our result by 6 in order to get the true set of combinations of 3 objects out of 5. We get $\frac{60}{6} = \boxed{10}$. □

Notice how the final computation was $\frac{5!}{3!(5-3)!}$. You will prove as a practice problem that the number of ways to choose k objects from a set of n objects is

$$\frac{n!}{k!(n-k)!}.$$

This should make some intuitive sense from the counting argument in the last problem. Now that we have some intuition, let's define combinations:

> **Definition 43.1** — In mathematics, a combination is a selection of items from a collection, such that the order of selection does not matter. The formula for combinations is similar to permutations but not exactly the same. It is, $_nC_k = \frac{n!}{k! \cdot (n-k!)}$. The value $_nC_k$ is also represented as $\binom{n}{k}$.

Looking at the formulas, we can see that the conditions for permutations and combinations are different. When we solve a permutation, the order in which the set is arranged matters, but in combinations, it doesn't matter.

Let's start with a problem to help us understand how combinations work.

> **Problem 233**
>
> Given the letters A, B, C, find the number ways that you can choose 2 of those letters without care of their order.

Proof. In this problem, we can't use permutations. Because the order for how the set is arranged doesn't matter, then plug the necessary values into the equation. Looking at the letters, there are three of them, so $n = 3$. The k value in this case would just be 2. If we plug this back into the equation, we get $\frac{3!}{2! \cdot (3-2)!}$. If we simplify this, we get that the answer for this problem is $\boxed{3}$. If we want to check if we got the we can manually pair up the letters to check. If we do, we get the pairs, AB, AC, and BC. □

> **Problem 234**
>
> Compute: $\binom{6}{1}$.

Proof. In this problem, we need to use the equation that was explained at the the beginning. The equation is, $\frac{n!}{k!\cdot(n-k)!}$. If we substitute the values into the equation, we get $\frac{(6)!}{1!\cdot(6-1)!}$. If we simplify this, we get, $\frac{(6)!}{1\cdot5!}$. If we simplify this again, then we get $\frac{6!}{5!}$, which can be written as $\frac{6\cdot5!}{5!}$. If we get rid of the 5! in both the numerator and denominator, we get the answer, $\boxed{6}$. $\qquad\square$

Problem 235

Compute: $\binom{9}{3}$

Proof. In this problem, just like that last one, we have to substitute the the values of the standard form of the combination into the equation. If we do that, we get the equation, $_9C_3 = \frac{(9!)}{3!\cdot(9-3)!}$. Now, if we simplify this equation, we get $\frac{9!}{3!6!}$. If we simplify the equation, we get $\frac{(}{9}\cdot 8\cdot 7\cdot 6!)6!\cdot 3\cdot 2\cdot 2$. We can cancel the 6! from both the numerator and the denominator. We can also cancel the 3 from the denominator with 9 from the numerator and 2 from the denominator with 8 from the numerator. Now, we are left with the expression, $3\cdot 2\cdot 7$. If we simplify this, we get the answer, $\boxed{42}$. $\qquad\square$

Problem 236

Compute: $\binom{18}{15}$.

Proof. In this problem, like the last, we need to take our standard form and substitute the values into the equation. If we substitute the values, we get the equation, $_{18}C_{15} = \frac{18!}{15!\cdot(18-15)!}$. If we simplify this, we get the equation, $\frac{18!}{15!\cdot3!}$. We can then simplify it to $\frac{18\cdot17\cdot16\cdot15!}{3\cdot2\cdot1\cdot15!}$. We can then cancel the 15! from both the numerator and the denominator. We can also cancel the 3 in the denominator with the 18 in the numerator and the 2 in the denominator with the 16 in the numerator. If we do this, we get the expression, $9\cdot 17\cdot 8$. If we simplify this, we get the answer, $\boxed{1224}$. $\qquad\square$

§43.1 Combinations Problems

Problem 237

Prove that
$$\binom{n}{k} = \frac{n!}{n!(n-k)!}.$$

(Hint: Look to the first problem in the section for guidance.)

Problem 238

In how many ways can you choose 3 letters from the letters A, B, C, D, E, F, G, H?

Problem 239

Compute: $\binom{20}{10}$.

Problem 240

Compute: $\binom{15}{8}$.

Problem 241

Compute: $\binom{30}{22}$.

§44 Pascal's Triangle

Pascal's Triangle is an interesting result from Combinations that can be used in algebraic expansions, as we will see.

There are many ways to define Pascal's Triangle, but we will be using one of those ways here. Rather than writing a rigorous definition, we will present the Pascal's triangle by making it from scratch. We start with

These are the first two rows. Now, we add another row. First, we start by adding 1's to the extreme left and extreme right of the row, like so:

At this point, it's just like the second row was repeated. Now, we add a 2 to the center of this row we just created:

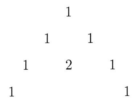

Why do we do this? Well, we actually add the two 1's on the top of this element in order to get this element. Now, we repeat the process for the next few rows. Hopefully, it will become more clear how we create the Pascal's Triangle.

We start by adding 1's on the far left and the far right of this new row once again.

$$
\begin{array}{ccccccc}
 & & & 1 & & & \\
 & & 1 & & 1 & & \\
 & 1 & & 2 & & 1 & \\
1 & & & & & & 1 \\
\end{array}
$$

From here, we wish to add the consecutive entries of the third row in order to get the missing elements of the fourth row. Specifically, we add $1 + 2 = 3$, where 1 is the first entry of the third row and 2 is the second entry of the third row. We then get 3 and put it in as the second entry of the fourth row, like so:

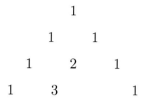

Notice how we sum the consecutive terms of each row to get the element in between and under them. We can similarly add $2+1=3$ to get the third element of the fourth row. Here, the 2 is the second element of the third row and the 1 is the third element of the third row. We can then put the resulting 3 under both of these, giving us the entire fourth row, like so:

We just keep doing this over and over again. There is no limit to how large the Pascal's Triangle can be, though we generally do not require too many rows for most purposes.

We can get the next row by first placing the 1's on either side of the new row. We get

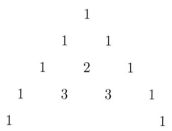

Now, we can add the consecutive elements in the fourth row to get the elements in the fifth row. We add $1+3=4, 3+3=6, 3+1=4$, and we fill the triangle correspondingly:

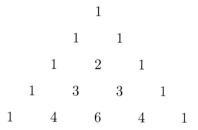

Make sure you see how we did this! To do the next row, we start with the 1's on either side:

```
                1
            1       1
         1     2     1
      1     3     3     1
   1     4     6     4     1
1                             1
```

Again, we sum the consecutive elements and we get $1+4=5, 4+6=10, 6+4=10, 4+1=5$, and we fill the triangle:

```
                  1
              1       1
           1     2     1
        1     3     3     1
     1     4     6     4     1
  1     5    10    10    5     1
```

Expanding this out for a few more rows (try this out on your own in the practice problems), we get

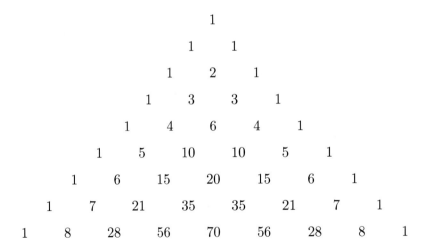

We will leave it at this for now.

§44.1 Pascal's Triangle Problems

Problem 242

Expand Pascal's Triangle for 10 rows.

§45 Binomial Theorem

The Binomial Theorem describes the expansion of powers of binomials. To use the binomial theorem, we need to be comfortable with Pascal's Triangle. Now, let's look at the proof for the binomial theorem.

Problem 243

Expand the binomial, $(a+b)^3$

Proof. We all know how to expand a binomial to the second power, but do we know how to expand a binomial to the third power, or the fourth power? Because we don't want to waste time manually expanding a binomial to power, we can use the binomial theorem. Now, let's look at the binomial pyramid:

$$
\begin{array}{ccccccc}
& & & 1 & & & \\
& & 1 & & 1 & & \\
& 1 & & 2 & & 1 & \\
1 & & 3 & & 3 & & 1 \\
\end{array}
$$

If you look at the fourth row of the pyramid, you see the numbers,

$$1 \qquad 3 \qquad 3 \qquad 1$$

These numbers represent the coefficients of a binomial to the third power. This means that if we want to expand the binomial, we get, $ab + 3ab + 3ab + ab$. Notice how all the variables are the same and there are no powers, this is because we have yet to figure out which variables go after each coefficient and with which power. Now, how do we decide. Let's compare our binomial to a binomial in the third power. The binomial is $a^2 + 2ab + b^2$. If we look at the binomial, what do we notice about the powers. As we go from left to right of the polynomial, the power on top of a is decreasing from 2 to 1 to finally 0. The opposite applies to the power on top of b. The powers are decreasing from right to left. So it goes from 2 to 1 and finally to 0.

Now, if we do the same for our current binomial, we can first write all the a's as

$$a^3 + a^2 + a + 1.$$

Now, let's add the b's to the binomial. If we do this, we get,

$$a^3 \cdot 1 + a^2 \cdot b + a \cdot b^2 \; 1 \cdot b^3.$$

Now, all that we need to do is to add the coefficients in front of each of the variables as we get that if we expand the binomial $(a+b)^3$, we get $\boxed{a^3 + 3a^2b + 3ab^2 + b^3}$. Proving the Binomial theorem is rather rigorous so we will just introduce how to use the theorem. $\quad\square$

Problem 244

Expand the binomial, $(a + b)^5$

Proof. Just like how we solved the last problem, we are going to use Pascal's triangle to solve this one. now, let's look at the triangle for a binomial to the fifth power.

$$
\begin{array}{ccccccccccc}
 & & & & & 1 & & & & & \\
 & & & & 1 & & 1 & & & & \\
 & & & 1 & & 2 & & 1 & & & \\
 & & 1 & & 3 & & 3 & & 1 & & \\
 & 1 & & 4 & & 6 & & 4 & & 1 & \\
1 & & 5 & & 10 & & 10 & & 5 & & 1 \\
\end{array}
$$

Now, we need to find which row matches the coefficients for the polynomial. In this, the sixth row is the one that we will use,

$$1 \quad 5 \quad 10 \quad 10 \quad 5 \quad 1$$

These coefficients will be in front of each term in the binomial once expanded. With the coefficients, the polynomial would look like, $ab + 5ab + 10ab + 10ab + 5ab + ab$. Keep in mind that this binomial is not the final answer, because we still need to find the powers, and as well the order in which we place the variables in each term. Now, let's find out in which order everything goes. Like the last problem, the powers of a decrease from left to right starting from 5 and the powers of b decrease from left to right.

Now, let's use this to expand the binomial. We can start by writing all the a's as,

$$a^5 + \quad +a^4 + \quad +a^3 + \quad +a^2 + \quad +a + \quad +1$$

Now, let's add the all the b values to the binomial. If we do this, we get,

$$a^5 \cdot 1 + \quad a^4 \cdot b + \quad a^3 \cdot b^2 + \quad a^2 \cdot b^3 + \quad b^4 \cdot a \quad + 1 \cdot b^5$$

Now that we have the terms with the powers sorted out, all that we need to do is to add the coefficients onto the terms. If we expand the binomial, $(a + b)^5$, we get the binomial,

$$\boxed{a^5 + 5a^4b + 10a^3b^2 + 10a^2b^3 + 5b^4a + b^5}$$

□

§45.1 Binomial Theorem Problems

Problem 245

Expand $(a + b)^2$ using the distributive property and the Binomial Theorem. How do your results compare?

Problem 246

Expand: $(2x + y)^4$ using the Binomial Theorem. (Hint: Treat $a = 2x$ and $b = y$ in the Binomial Theorem and plug it in to its respective variables!)

Problem 247

Expand: $(a + b)^6$.

§46 Introduction to Probability

As we said in the introduction, we will covering another aspect of Discrete Mathematics in this text. This is Probability. As we said before, Probability is the chance of something happening. This is a rather informal definition, but it is hard to convey the rigorous definition of what exactly Probability is. We can gain some understanding of it nonetheless by looking at some intuition around the subject, and this should be more than enough to solve problems on the AMC 8.

Let's establish this as well as a notation:

Definition 46.1 (Probability) — Informally, probability is defined as the chance of something happening. The probability of some event A happening is denoted as $P(A)$.

Let's try to get the hang of this through a few examples.

Problem 248

What is the probability of flipping a coin heads? In other words, what is $P(heads)$, where *heads* means getting a head after flipping a coin?

Proof. All this problem is asking us is: "What is the chance that on a given flip of a coin, we get heads?"

Well, at any given flip, there are 2 possibilities: heads or tails. Out of these 2 possibility, we will only get heads once, or 1 time. Therefore, we expect to get heads half $\left(\frac{1}{2}\right)$ the time and tails the other half of the time.

> **Remark 46.2.** This makes sense intuitively. This is also why we say that when we wish to choose one option out of two "at random" that we should flip a coin. This is because coin flips are said to be random - at any given flip, it is almost impossible to tell for sure what you will get.

So, the probability, or the chance, of flipping a head in a coin flip is $\boxed{\dfrac{1}{2}}$. Recall that this is the same as $\boxed{50\%}$. $\qquad\qquad\qquad\qquad\qquad\qquad\qquad\qquad\qquad\qquad$ $\square$

In the end of the last problem, why did we put a percentage answer? Why the hassle? Let's see why.

Problem 249

What is the smallest probability of some event. happening? In other words, what is the probability that something impossible happens?

What is the largest probability of some event happening? In other words, what is the probability that something certain happens?

Proof. In order to shed light on this problem, we use the coin example again, just with a small twist. We have a coin that has heads on both sides. Now, let's answer the questions in the problem.

The first question asks the probability of an impossible event happening. This is the same as asking:

"What is the probability/chance of getting a tails on a certain coin flip on the above described coin?"

Make sure how you see that this is essentially the same question. Well, because both sides are heads, it is **impossible** to get a tails on a certain coin flip. Therefore, the probability of this happening is $\boxed{0}$ or $\boxed{0\%}$.

On the other hand, the second question in the problem asks for the probability of a certain event happening. This would be the same as asking:

"What is the probability/chance of getting a heads on a certain coin flip on the above described coin?"

Well, our coin has heads on both sides, so no matter which side it lands on, we will always get heads. We say that this event is certain to happen if we flip a coin. Therefore the probability is $\boxed{1}$ (because we would expect this to happen once for every time we flip this coin. This is the same as $\boxed{100\%}$. □

> **Remark 46.3.** The lowest probability of something happening is 0 or 0%, while the greatest probability of something happening is 1 or 100%. This is why we often display probabilities in percents. Our answer will be on the scale of 0 to 100 percent.

Another way of thinking about probability (that we have been hinting towards in the last few problems) is the following:

> Definition 46.4 — (When each outcome is equally likely,) the probability of something happening can be expressed as
>
> $$\frac{\text{number of successes}}{\text{number of total possible outcomes}}.$$

Firstly, try not to worry too much yet about the small technicality in the parentheses just yet. We will look more into that in a later section. For now, let us use the analogy of coin flips.

When we wish to find the probability of a coin landing on heads, the number of successes would be the possible number of ways a coin can land on heads. We will now expand this to dice, another random generator.

> **Problem 250**
> What is the probability of getting a 1 when rolling a fair six-sided die?

Proof. We all know what die are. We have use them in playing board games before. Now, we are asked to find the probability, or the chance, of getting 1 when we roll this die.

We can use the last definition we came up with. We can calculate the number of possible ways to get 1, then we can divide our result by the total number of possible outcomes of a six-sided die.

The number of possible ways to get 1 is obviously 1 because there is only 1 side on a six-sided die that displays 1. Furthermore, the number of possible outcomes on a six-sided die is simply 6 (because there are six sides).

Therefore, our answer is $1 \div 6 = \boxed{\dfrac{1}{6}} \approx \boxed{0.167} = \boxed{16.7\%}$, where the $\approx$ symbol means that we are estimating our answer for the last two. □

We have seen 50% and even 16.7%, but what do these mean? In other words, how would we communicate our results to someone else without being technical and using the actual percentage?

Remark 46.5. There are a couple of terms that we use to describe different probabilities. If we wish to find the probability of the event A happening, then:

- If $P(A) = 0\%$, then the probability, or the chance of event A happening is **impossible**.

- If $0\% < P(A) < 50\%$, then we say that the event A is **unlikely**, meaning that it probably won't happen.

- If $P(A) = 50\%$, then we say that there is an equal chance of $P(A)$ happening or not happening. Therefore, it is **equally likely**.

- If $50\% < P(A) < 100\%$, then we say that the event A is **likely**, meaning that it will probably happen.

- If $P(A) = 100\%$, then the probability, or the chance of event A happening is **certain**, because it will always happen.

This last remark is something to take note of. It's all well and good that we are able to compute probabilities, but it does not mean anything if we are not able to put it into layman's terms and communicate our results.

§47 Multiplying Probabilities

We multiply two probabilities, when we want to or more things to happen "at the same time" or consecutively. One of the most important things to remember when multiplying probabilities is that the outcomes are independent of each other. Consider two events, A and B, which are independent of each other. These events where one event is independent of the other is called uncorrelated because it doesn't matter about what the outcome of one event is because it doesn't effect the other.

Problem 251

What is the chance that the both times you flip a coin, they land on heads?

Proof. In this problem, we can call the first flip event A and the second flip event B. If we look at the different combinations of the two events, we see that the different combinations that you can get are HH, HT, TH, TT. Out of all 4 outcomes, it is clear that only 1 out of the 4 ways is the condition that we want. We can write this as there is a $\boxed{\dfrac{1}{4}}$ chance of getting a HH.

We can look at it this way, but if we want to use the method of multiplying probabilities, we can consider each event. There is a $\frac{1}{2}$ chance that it lands on heads and a $\frac{1}{2}$ that it lands on heads a second time. If we multiply these two probabilities, we get that the probability for both turns to land on heads is $\boxed{\dfrac{1}{4}}$. □

Problem 252

Find the probability of rolling a 12 with two-six sided dice.

Proof. We present three solutions for this problem:

Solution 1 To solve this problem, we have to look at each individual event and then multiply them together. In our case, there is only one way to get a 12 (6 - 6). This out of 36 total possibilities (anything - anything). Because of this, the probability is $\boxed{\dfrac{1}{36}}$.

Solution 2 If we do it this way, we don't utilize the multiplication rule. To we use the multiplication rule, we have to look at each individual dice that is rolled. Because to get a 12, we a need a 6 and 6 on both dice, this means that the probability is $\frac{1}{6}$ for the first roll and $\frac{1}{6}$ for the second role. If we multiply this, we get $\frac{1}{6} \cdot \frac{1}{6}$ or $\boxed{\dfrac{1}{36}}$.

Solution 3 Another way that we could solve this problem is to use the table below.

+	1	2	3	4	5	6
1	2	3	4	5	6	7
2	3	4	5	6	7	8
3	4	5	6	7	8	9
4	5	6	7	8	9	10
5	6	7	8	9	10	11
6	7	8	9	10	11	12

Looking at the table, we see that out of all the possibilities, there is only one way to to get 12 out all 36 ways so the probability that that the sum of the two dice is $\boxed{\dfrac{1}{36}}$. □

Problem 253

There are 3 six-sided dice that are rolled. What is the probability that at least one comes up with a 5 or 6?

Proof. When looking at this problem, you think that we need to separately consider each case but that actually only makes it more difficult. The easiest way to solve this is to consider the chance the we do not end up with a 5 or 6 in any of the cases and take that value and subtract that from 1. There is a 4 out of 6 or $\frac{2}{3}$ chance that a dice does not land on a 5 or 6. Now, we have 3 dice so have to multiply $\frac{2}{3} \cdot \frac{2}{3} \cdot \frac{2}{3}$. This is the probability that the three dices do not land on 5 or 6. Now, we have to take this value and subtract it from one so we get the expression.

$$P(\text{at least one 5 or 6}) = 1 - P(\text{no 5 or 6}) = 1 - \left(\frac{2}{3} \cdot \frac{2}{3} \cdot \frac{2}{3}\right)$$

If we do this we get the answer $\boxed{\dfrac{19}{27}}$. The method we used here utilized the multiplication rule as well as a theorem called the complementary theorem which has the formula $P(A) = 1 - P(\text{not } A)$. We will learn this later on. $\square$

Problem 254

Two cards are drawn from a standard deck of cards. What is the probability that the first is a spade and the second is a heart.

Proof. To solve this problem, we have to look at each individual case and multiply the individual probabilities. The first event is the probability of a spade. There are 52 cards in a standard deck. Out of these there are 13 cards which are spades. This means that there is a $\frac{13}{52}$ or $\frac{1}{4}$. Now of the remaining 51 cards, there are 13 heart cards so probability is $\frac{13}{51}$. If we multiply these two values, we get that the probability of getting a spade and then heart is $\frac{1}{4} \cdot \frac{13}{51}$ or $\boxed{\dfrac{13}{204}}$. $\square$

§48 Adding Probabilities

Unlike multiplying probabilities, you add probabilities when the two events are alternatives also known as mutually exclusive. Like the name states, mutually exclusive means that the two events cannot happen at the same time. This means that to find the probabilities, we need to add them rather than multiply them. Now, let's look at some problems.

Problem 255

In a dice roll, find P(1 or 3).

Proof. In this problem, like multiplying probabilities, we have to find the individual probabilities, but this time, we add them. Let's first look at P(1). There is a one is 6 chance or $\frac{1}{6}$. Now, let's look at P(3). Like getting a 1, there is one a one in 6 chance that we get a 3 or $\frac{1}{6}$. If we add them up, we get $\frac{1}{6} + \frac{1}{6}$ or $\boxed{\frac{1}{3}}$. □

> **Remark 48.1.** "Or" is a key word that tells us to add probabilities (typically).
>
> "And" is a key word that tells us to multiply probabilities (typically), as we saw in the last section.
>
> Notice how this is true. It will become much easier to realize which one to use in problems if you do so. Also, do not memorize these! These rules, while typically true, could have exceptions. Keep an eye out for that. ☺

Problem 256

Compute:
$$P(1 \text{ or an even number on a dice roll}).$$

Proof. Remember, the word "or" means that we add our probabilities. Basically, we add the probability of getting a 1 to the probability of getting an even number on a dice roll.

There is 1 way to get 1 out of 6 possible outcomes on a die, or a probability of $\frac{1}{6}$. Additionally, there are 3 out of 6 possible ways to get an even number on a dice roll. This is $\frac{1}{2}$. Adding these, we get $\frac{1}{6} + \frac{1}{2} = \frac{4}{6} = \boxed{\frac{2}{3}}$. □

Notice how in the last problem, 1 is not even. This is extremely important, as we will see in the next problem.

Problem 257

Compute:
$$P(1 \text{ or an odd number on a dice roll}).$$

Proof. In this case, we cannot simply add the probabilities of getting a 1 and getting an odd number. This is because **1 is an odd number itself**. If we counted these both separately and added them, we would be **overcounting** the possibility of getting a 1 on a dice roll. Instead. There are a total of 3 ways to get an odd number *or* 1, namely by getting either of 1, 3, 5. **This is the combined set of 1 and the number of odd numbers on a die.** We also have 6 possible outcomes (because of the six sides of a die), so our probability is

$\frac{3}{6} = \boxed{\frac{1}{2}}$. $\qquad\qquad\qquad\qquad\qquad\qquad\qquad\qquad\qquad\qquad\qquad\qquad$ $\square$

Make sure you understand the solution in the last problem and why it is not ok to simply add the probabilities of two events just based on the word "or".

Problem 258

You have a bag of marbles with colors green, red, and blue. There are 3 blue marbles, 2 green marbles, and 5 red marbles. What is the probability that you get either a green or a red marble?

Proof. To solve this, we need to find the probability of us getting each type of colored marble. For the the green marble, there are 2 out of 10 total marbles, so this means that the chance that we pick out a green marble is $\frac{2}{10}$. Next, we have to look at the chance that we land on a red marble. There are 5 red marbles out of 10 marbles in total. This means that there is a $\frac{5}{10}$ chance that we land on a red marble. Because we have to find the probability that we have to land on either the green or the red, we have to add up the two probabilities.

This means that we get that the chance that we land on a green or a red marble is $\boxed{\frac{7}{10}}$ or

$\boxed{70\%}$. $\qquad\qquad\qquad\qquad\qquad\qquad\qquad\qquad\qquad\qquad\qquad\qquad\qquad\qquad$ $\square$

§49 Casework

A lot of problems in both probability and counting have cases which come down to evaluating different cases. To find the probability of the overall value, we need to first find the values of each individual probabilities and then add then up. Now, let's look at some problems.

Problem 259

There is a 20% chance it will rain today. If it rains, there is a 10% chance that we will be allowed to go outside; otherwise, there is an 80% chance we will be able to go outside. What is the probability that we will be allowed to go outside?

Proof. When you first read this problem, it may seem very complicated and hard to solve. To break down the complicated problem, we will first have to slit up the overall case into multiply different cases and find the probabilities for each of those. To solve this problem, we slit it up into into the cases that it rains and that it doesn't rain. The probability that it rains **and** we go outside is $(0.20) \cdot (0.10) = 0.02$. Notice that that when there is an **and**, we need to multiply and when there is an **or**, we add the probabilities. The probability that it doesn't rain and that we can go outside is $(1 - 0.20) \cdot (0.80) = 0.64$. The overall probability that we go outside is the sum of these, or $0.64 + 0.02 = \boxed{0.66}$. □

Problem 260 (Art of Problem Solving)

What is the probability of rolling a 12 if three six-sided dice are rolled?

Proof. Now we will have some nontrivial cases. Let's consider the first two dice as a unit, and the third by itself. Then the configurations which yield 12 are 6-6, 7-5, 8-4, 9-3, 10-2, and 11-1. Using this, we can write down the probability for each case.

+	1	2	3	4	5	6
1	2	3	4	5	6	7
2	3	4	5	6	7	8
3	4	5	6	7	8	9
4	5	6	7	8	9	10
5	6	7	8	9	10	11
6	7	8	9	10	11	12

Looking at this table, we see that for 6-6, it is $\left(\frac{5}{36}\right) \cdot \left(\frac{1}{6}\right)$, since the probability of getting a 12 using both dice is $\frac{5}{36}$ and the probability of getting a 6 is $\frac{1}{6}$. The rest of the cases are done exactly the same.

$$P(6-6) \; + \; P(7-5) \; + \; P(8-4) \; + \; P(9-3) \; + \; P(9-3) \; + \; P(10-2) \; + \; P(11-2) =$$

$$\frac{5}{36} \cdot \frac{1}{6} \; + \; \frac{6}{36} \cdot \frac{1}{6} \; + \; \frac{5}{36} \cdot \frac{1}{6} \; + \; \frac{4}{36} \cdot \frac{1}{6} \; + \; \frac{3}{36} \cdot \frac{1}{6} \; + \; \frac{2}{36} \cdot \frac{1}{6} \; + \; \frac{1}{36} \cdot \frac{1}{6} \; = \; \boxed{\frac{25}{216}}.$$

□

§50 Complementary Counting

There is a rather interesting strategy in Probability called "complementary Counting." To develop this strategy, let us see a rather intuitive yet powerful concept.

Problem 261

What is $P(A) + P(\text{not } A)$? What does this mean?

Proof. This is easier to evaluate when we try to understand what this means. P(A) is the probability that event A happens. On the other hand, P(not A) is the probability that event A does not happen.

Thinking about this intuitively, we see that there are only two alternatives in the universe with respect to event A:

- Event A happens;

- Otherwise, event A does not happen.

Now, when we add these two probabilities up, we are finding the probability that event A happens or event A does not happen. Obviously, the chance of either one of these happening is certain, or $\boxed{1}$, no matter what A is. □

> **Remark 50.1.** From the last problem, we have that
>
> $$P(A) + P(\text{not } A) = 1.$$
>
> More commonly, we use the relationship in the different form
>
> $$P(A) = 1 - P(\text{not } A).$$
>
> This means that the probability of some event A happening is 1 minus the probability of it not happening.

Ok, great! Now, why is this useful?

Well, just as in counting, sometimes the probability that something does not happen is easier to find than the probability of an event itself. Let's try an example.

Problem 262

What is the probability that on 3 coin flips (on a fair coin) that you get at least 1 heads.

Proof. We could go about casework and compute:

- The probability that we get 1 head;

- The probability that we get 2 heads;

- The probability that we get 3 heads (on all 3 flips).

Well, no. That would take too long. Then, what?

Wait a minute! What if we just consider the probability that we get no heads at all? Then, we have that (from the last problem)

$$P(\text{at least one head}) = 1 - P([\text{not}] \text{ at least one head})$$

or more simply

$$P(\text{at least one head}) = 1 - P(\text{no heads}).$$

We know how to evaluate P(no heads). Specifically, in order for this to happen, we must have that we get tails on every one of the 3 coin flips.

So, the problem is now: "What is the probability that on 3 coin flips that we get tails every single time?"

This is an "and" problem. This means that we have to multiply the probabilities. The probability that we get tails the first time is $\frac{1}{2}$. Similarly, the probability of getting tails on the second or third time is also $\frac{1}{2}$. Therefore, the probability that we get tails on the first flip **and** tails on the second flip **and** tails on the third flip is

$$\frac{1}{2} \cdot \frac{1}{2} \cdot \frac{1}{2} = \frac{1}{8}.$$

Now, we go back to our original problem.

> **Remark 50.2.** Always keep in mind what you are solving for, especially in complementary counting.
>
> Additionally, it is good practice to read the question one more time before you answer to assure yourself you answered correctly.

We bring back the relation we found before:

$$P(\text{at least one head}) = 1 - P(\text{no heads}).$$

Substituting our acquired knowledge that P(no heads) $= \frac{1}{8}$, we find that

$$P(\text{at least one head}) = 1 - \frac{1}{8} = \boxed{\frac{7}{8}}.$$

$\square$

Let's try another example to become more proficient.

§50.1 Complimentary Counting Problems

Problem 263

I rolled a fair dice 5 times. What is the probability that got a number greater than 2 at least once?

§51 Counting and Probability Problems

Here is a compilation of Counting and Probability Problems that you should be able to solve. These problems are in random order.

Warning: Some problems may require proactive manipulation of the taught techniques. ☺

Problem 264 (AMC 8 2016: Problem 13)

Two different numbers are randomly selected from the set $-2, -1, 0, 3, 4, 5$ and multiplied together. What is the probability that the product is 0?

Problem 265 (AMC 8 2016: Problem 21)

A top hat contains 3 red chips and 2 green chips. Chips are drawn randomly, one at a time without replacement, until all 3 of the reds are drawn or until both green chips are drawn. What is the probability that the 3 reds are drawn?

Problem 266 (AMC 8 2001: Problem 18)

Two dice are thrown. What is the probability that the product of the two numbers is a multiple of 5?

Problem 267 (AMC 8 2014: Problem 12)

A magazine printed photos of three celebrities along with three photos of the celebrities as babies. The baby pictures did not identify the celebrities. Readers were asked to match each celebrity with the correct baby pictures. What is the probability that a reader guessing at random will match all three correctly?

Problem 268 (AMC 8 2002: Problem 12)

A board game spinner is divided into three regions labeled A, B and C. The probability of the arrow stopping on region A is $\frac{1}{3}$ and on region B is $\frac{1}{2}$. The probability of the arrow stopping on region C is?

Problem 269 (AMC 8 2002: Problem 19)

How many whole numbers between 99 and 999 contain exactly one 0? (Hint: Try counting in cases. How many numbers in this range have a 0 in the ones place? How many numbers in this range have a 0 in the tens place? Can there be a 0 in the hundreds place as well?) (Note: All of the numbers in the range given in this problem have 3 digits except for 99, the largest 2 digit number.)

Problem 270 (AMC 8 2017: Problem 9)

All of Macy's marbles are blue, red, green, or yellow. One third of her marbles are blue, one fourth of them are red, and six of them are green. What is the smallest number of yellow marbles that Macy could have?

Problem 271 (AMC 8 2002: Problem 21)

Harold tosses a nickel four times. The probability that he gets at least as many heads as tails is? (Hint: There must be 2 heads and 2 tails in order for this to happen. What is the probability that he gets a certain arrangement of 2 heads and 2 tails on 4 coin flips? In how many different ways can the 2 heads and 2 tails be arranged?)

Problem 272 (AMC 8 2003: Problem 12)

When a fair six-sided die is tossed on a table top, the bottom face cannot be seen. What is the probability that the product of the numbers on the five faces that can be seen is divisible by 6? (Hint: If 6 is not hidden, then the product is obviously divisible by 6. What about when the 6 is hidden?)

Problem 273 (AMC 8 2011: Problem 12)

Angie, Bridget, Carlos, and Diego are seated at random around a square table, one person to a side. What is the probability that Angie and Carlos are seated opposite each other?

Problem 274 (AMC 8 2004: Problem 2)

How many different four-digit numbers can be formed by rearranging the four digits in 2004? (Hint: A number with zeros in the beginning such as 0024 does not count as a four digit number because 0024 = 24, which has 2 digits. Keep this in mind.)

Problem 275 (AMC 8 2004: Problem 5)

Ms. Hamilton's eighth-grade class wants to participate in the annual three-person-team basketball tournament. Lance, Sally, Joy, and Fred are chosen for the team. In how many ways can the three starters be chosen? (Hint: You are choosing some number of people from a larger group of people.)

Problem 276 (AMC 8 2004: Problem 8)

Find the number of two-digit positive integers whose digits total 7. (Hint: This is similar to the dice rolling problem.)

Problem 277

Three friends have a total of 6 identical pencils, and each one has at least one pencil. In how many ways can this happen? (Hint: Consider stealing their pencils and redistributing it back to them. In how many ways can you do this? Notice how this is the same problem. Also remember to take into account that the pencils are identical.)

Problem 278 (AMC 8 2015: Problem 7)

Each of two boxes contains three chips numbered 1, 2, 3. A chip is drawn randomly from each box and the numbers on the two chips are multiplied. What is the probability that their product is even?

Problem 279 (AMC 8 2005: Problem 18)

How many three-digit numbers are divisible by 13? (Hint: Consider the smallest and largest such numbers and use these to count the rest of the numbers.)

Problem 280 (AMC 8 2006: Problem 11)

How many two-digit numbers have digits whose sum is a perfect square? (Hint: What is the largest possible sum of the digits of a two-digit number? How many perfect squares are there less than this?)

Problem 281 (AMC 8 2007: Problem 21)

Two cards are dealt from a deck of four red cards labeled A, B, C, D and four green cards labeled A, B, C, D. A winning pair is two of the same color or two of the same letter. What is the probability of drawing a winning pair? (Hint: Keyword "or." Can you get two cards of the same color **and** the same letter? Or are they independent events?)

Part VI
Geometry in the AMC 8

§52 Introduction

Next in our adventures of conquering the AMC 8, we arrive at Geometry, the subject of studying shapes... essentially. Geometry can get very complex, so we will just be touching upon its basics here. However, this should be enough for you to solve most geometry problems on the AMC 8.

> **Remark 52.1** (Euclid's Postulates). Euclid, a Greek mathematician, is sometimes considered the father of Geometry. He once proposed that everything in Geometry could be derived from very simple axioms, or assumptions. These axioms were:
>
> - A straight line segment can be drawn joining any two points.
>
> - Any straight line segment can be extended indefinitely in a straight line.
>
> - Given any straight lines segment, a circle can be drawn having the segment as radius and one endpoint as center.
>
> - All Right Angles are congruent.
>
> - If two lines are drawn which intersect a third in such a way that the sum of the inner angles on one side is less than two Right Angles, then the two lines inevitably must intersect each other on that side if extended far enough. This postulate is equivalent to what is known as the Parallel Postulate.
>
> Do not worry if you do not understand some of this terminology just yet.
>
> Seeing such basic axioms, or "postulates," how could one come up with any Geometric relationships at all? Well,
>
> Euclid's idea was to prove simple relationships from these basics, and then use **those** simple relationships to prove even more relationships, and use **those** to prove even more...
>
> Euclid wrote a book on this called *Euclid's Elements*, whose ideas are still in practice today.

§53 Basic Definitions

Before we get to the fun stuff, there are a few definitions that we must see first. Some of these are fairly obvious as you may have seen them before. Nonetheless, you should pay attention to all of these because they are used heavily in Geometry. We start off easy, then go from there. Most of these definitions are rather informal simply to give you intuition about what they are.

> **Definition 53.1** (Point) — A point is a location in space and is represented by a dot,

like so:

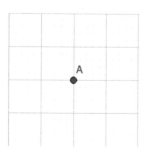

Also, like in the picture, we commonly label points with capital letters such as A. (This is not a hard and fast rule, just a tradition.)

What about if we have 2 points?

Definition 53.2 (Line Segment) — A line segment is formed through the connection of two points, which are called the line segment's end points.

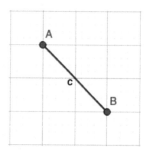

We can refer to a line segment by either using its end points or labeling it using a lower case letter (also not a strict rule). So, we can refer to the above line segment as line segment $\overline{AB}$ or line segment c.

We can also extend a line segment forever.

Definition 53.3 (Line) — A line is a line segment that extends forever in both directions. Since we obviously cannot draw a line segment that goes on forever, we use arrows on bot sides of a line to indicate that it continues past the arrows forever, like so:

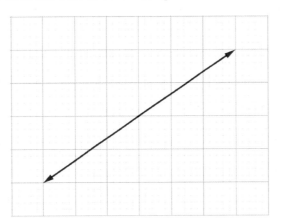

We can use two points on the line to refer to it. For example, the following line could be referred to as $\overleftrightarrow{CD}$ because the points C and D are on the line.

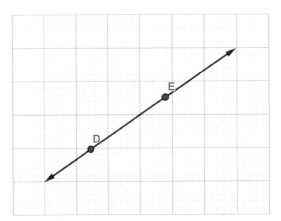

Notice how we put the arrows in $\overleftrightarrow{CD}$ in both directions because we extend the line in both directions.

Instead of extending a line segment forever in both directions, we can extend it forever in just one direction.

Definition 53.4 (Ray) — A ray is a line segment extended forever in only one direction.

We can denote the following ray as $\overrightarrow{AC}$.

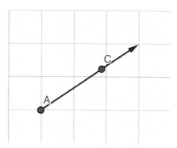

Here, A is called the endpoint of the ray, just like the endpoint of a line segment. The point C is another point on this ray, meaning that we can use these two points to refer to the ray. Notice how we put the arrow in $\overrightarrow{AC}$ toward the C to show that we extend the ray in the direction of the point C tarting from the point A.

What if we have two intersecting lines, line segments, or rays?

Remark 53.5. We often refer to lines, line segments, and rays as simply lines. While this may not be technically correct, it is simpler to communicate. You can usually use context to understand which one is being referred to. However, if there is not enough context, the type will likely be specified.

Definition 53.6 (Angles) — An angle is formed by the intersection of two lines. We can refer to angles by the lines and points on those lines that make the angles. For example, we can refer to the following angle as $\angle CAD$ because it is made of the points C, A, D. Notice how we put A in the middle because that is the location at which the angle actually is.

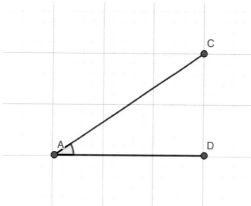

We can quantitatively measure how large, or wide, these angles are. To do this, we start with circles.

Definition 53.7 (Degrees) — We can use Degrees to describe the "wideness" of an angle. In a circle, there are 360 degrees. So, if we went the whole way around the circle and came back to the same point, we will have measured exactly 360 degrees.

In the above picture, if we start measuring the angle from D and go all the way around until we reach D again, we will have counted 360 degrees. This angle is called a **round angle**. Intuitively you may have guessed that if we instead went $\frac{1}{360}$ths of the way around the same point A, we will have counted only 1 degree. Similarly, if we want 180 degrees, we just go around half the way and we get a **straight angle**, like the one below.

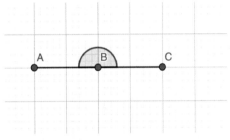

Remember, this is because $180 = \frac{1}{2} \cdot 360$, or $\frac{1}{2}$ of the way around the circle. This is called a straight angle because it is kind of made by a straight line. Specifically, there is a "straight" line that goes through points A, B, C.

Ok, now what about going a fourth of the way around the circle? Well, this would be $\frac{1}{4} \cdot 360 = 90$ degrees. Hopefully, you are catching onto what we're doing here. A 90 degree angle is often called a **right angle** and has many unique properties, some of which we will explore in the next section. A 90 degree angle is drawn below.

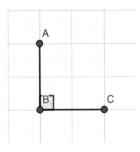

This is almost needless to say, but an angle of 0 degrees occurs when we do not go about the circle at all counting any degrees! Look at the following image.

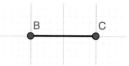

The angle is absolutely nothing at all! In fact, this is just one line segment. ☺

We also have special names for angles that are less than 180 degrees. If our angle is more than 0 degrees but less than 90 degrees (or a quarter circle), we say that the angle is an **acute angle**. The following is an example of an acute angle.

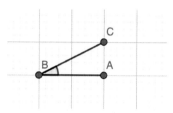

On the other hand, if an angle is between 90 degrees and 180 degrees, then we say that the angle is an **obtuse angle**. The following is an example of an obtuse angle.

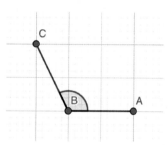

If an angle is greater than 180 degrees but less than 360 degrees, then we call the angle a **reflex angle**. The following is an example of a reflex angle.

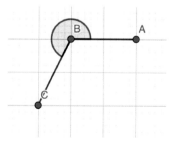

When we say that some angle is more than something but less than another thing, imagine how much around the circle you have to go. This way, the images presented will make more sense.

One final note: instead of saying "degrees," *degrees*, *degrees*, **degrees** all the time, we use a special notation. If we wanted to say 90 degrees, we could instead say $90°$. This is much more compact and we will often use it instead of writing out the word "degrees."

This last "definition," or list of definitions, should have given you some intuition on what degrees are. It is hard to define degrees without knowing much about geometry, but we did our best here to convey some basic intuition. ☺

Try out these practice problems to see if you get the gist of it.

> **Remark 53.8.** While it is nice to know about all of these different types of angles, the main ones in Geometry will be acute angles, right, angles, and obtuse angles. Again, other angles have their moments, but these three are generally the most popular.

§53.1 Basic Definitions Problems

Problem 282

What angle is $\frac{1}{8}$th of the way around the circle?

Problem 283

What angle is $\frac{3}{4}$ths of the way around the circle?

Problem 284

What kind of angle is the following?

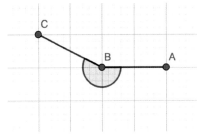

Problem 285

What kind of angle is the following?

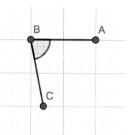

§54 The Pythagorean Theorem

Theorem 54.1 (The Pythagorean Theorem)

The Pythagorean Theorem states that the sum of the squares of the legs of a right triangle is equivalent to the square of the hypotenuse.

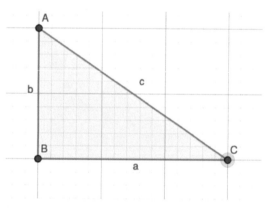

In the above image, this would mean that $a^2 + b^2 = c^2$.

This triangle is how the triangle would look like to use the Pythagorean triangle. Although it is not included in this image, this triangle is actually a right triangle. The Pythagorean Theorem only works on right triangles and if the triangle is not a right triangle, the answer you get using this theorem will not be correct.

To sense why this might be true, let's look at an image. (The following is not a proof.)

163

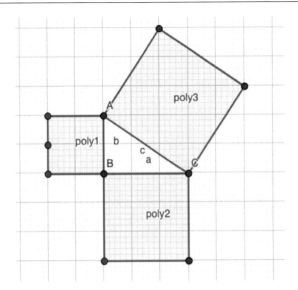

In this image, the first square, poly1, has side length a. This means that the area of this square is a^2. Next, let's look at poly2. It has a side length of b, giving it an area of b^2. Finally, let's look at poly3. This has an area of c^2. We can see that the combined area of the smaller squares is about the area of the larger square, suggesting that $a^2 + b^2 = c^2$ is true. This is not a formal proof, just a basic intuition on how the Pythagorean Theorem might be true.

While we do not prove it here, we can assure you that the Pythagorean Theorem holds. This theorem is arguably one of the most significant in all of Geometry.

Problem 286

Using the Pythagorean Theorem, find the length of the hypotenuse of a right triangle, given that the legs have length is 3 and 4.

Remark 54.2. The hypotenuse of a right triangle is often denoted with the letter c. Similarly, the legs of a right triangle are often denoted with the letters a and b. Therefore, the Pythagorean Theorem tells us that $a^2 + b^2 = c^2$. We will be using this convention here.

We know that the equation for the Pythagorean Theorem is $a^2 + b^2 = c^2$. We also know that a is 3 and b is 4. We can use these values and plug them into the equation to find for the value of c. If we plug them in, we get, $3^2 + 4^2 = c^2$. If we solve for c, we get the equation, $9 + 16 = c^2$. Then we can say that $c^2 = 25$. If we take the square root of both sides, we get that c is equal to $\boxed{5}$. □

Problem 287

If we are given that c is 64 and b is 32, find a.

Proof. Proof. Like that last problem, we can substitute the values for c and b into the equation and solve for a. If we do that, we get the equation, $64^2 = 32^2 + a^2$. We can now solve for a. If we isolate. a, we get the equation $a = \sqrt{64^2 - 32^2}$. If we solve for a using this equation, we get that a is equal to, $\boxed{55.42}$.

> **Remark 54.3.** Notice how we do not always get a whole number when using the Pythagorean Theorem. Even though the triangle is a right triangle, this does not mean that all the side lengths have to be whole numbers.

$\square$

Definition 54.4 — A Pythagorean triple consists of three positive integers a, b, and c, such that $a^2 + b^2 = c^2$. If (a, b, c) is a Pythagorean triple, then so is (ka, kb, kc) for any positive integer k. When $\gcd(a, b, c) = 1$, (a, b, c) is a **primitive Pythagorean triple**.

Example of primitive Pythagorean triples include

$$(3, 4, 5);$$

$$(5, 12, 13);$$

$$(7, 24, 25);$$

$$(8, 15, 17);$$

$$(9, 40, 41).$$

These are the most widely used Pythagorean triples, but there are many more (infinitely more in fact). All the problems that we will solve will use these 5 Pythagorean triples.

Using these triples (which you should memorize by heart), let's solve some problems!

Problem 288

Using you knowledge on Pythagorean triples, find out what the value of b is given that a is 12 and c is 20 without using the Pythagorean Theorem.

Proof. When solving this problem, we can only use our knowledge on the Pythagorean Theorems. That means that the values of a, b, and c must be related to a Pythagorean triple. We know that the values $a = 3$, $b = 4$, and $c = 5$, make a Pythagorean triple. If we compare our values of a, b, and c to the given values for a and c, we notice that we multiply the original triple values by 4 to get the new values. $3 \cdot 4 = 12$, and $5 \cdot 4 = 20$. This also means that to find b, we need to multiply the original side length of 4 by 4. If we do this, we get that the value for be is $4 \cdot 4 = \boxed{16}$.

If we want to check to see if the answer we got is correct, we can simply use the Pythagorean Theorem. If we plug in the values of a, b, and c into the equation, we would get $20^2 = 12^2 + 16^2$. If we simplify this, we get the equation, $400 = 144 + 256$, which if simplified gives us $200 = 200$. This proves that the values that we got are correct. $\square$

Problem 289

Using the Pythagorean triples, find the value of c if you are given that a is 27 and b is 120 without using the Pythagorean Theorem.

Proof. Like that last problem, we need to solve this without using the Pythagorean Theorem. We can do this by finding out which Pythagorean triple the values that we are given is related to. We can do this by looking at the value of a. We notice 27 is $9 \cdot 3$. If we look at the list of Pythagorean triples, we can see that 27 is related to 9 which is part of the Pythagorean triple $9, 40, 41$. If we also look at the value for b which is 120 is 3 times 40. Looking at this, we can deduce that each to find the new values of a, b, and c, we need to multiply the original values by 3. This means that to find c, we multiply 41 by 3 to get $41 \cdot 3 = \boxed{123}$.

To make sure that we got the correct answer, we can use the Pythagorean Theorem. We now have the values of a, b, and c, so we can plug it into the equation. If we do, we get $123^2 = 27^2 + 120^2$. If we simplify this, we get $15129 = 14400 + 729$. If we simplify this even further, we get the equation, $15129 = 15129$. This proves that the values that we got are correct. $\square$

§55 Area of Triangles

The area of a triangle like the area of other shapes is used to find out the total amount of space the shape takes up on a plane. To find the area of a triangle, let's look at this image.

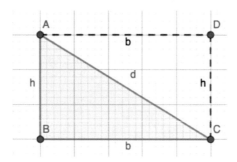

If we look at this image, we see that we made a rectangle out of the triangle. We did this so that we can prove the area of a triangle. Before we find the area of the triangle, we need to find the area of the rectangle. We know that the area of the rectangle is the base · height. In this case, the area of the rectangle would be $b \cdot h$ units^2. We found the area of the rectangle, now we need to find the area of the triangle. Looking at the image, we see that the triangle is half the area of the rectangle. This means that the area of triangle is $\frac{b \cdot h}{2}$ units^2.

Problem 290

Find the area of the triangle:

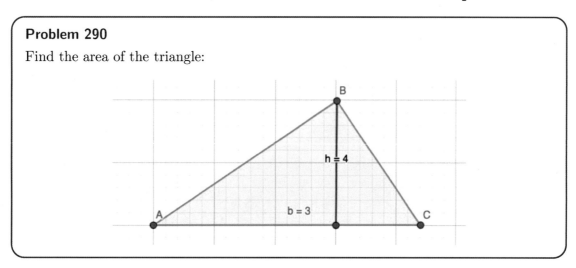

Proof. Looking at the triangle, we see that we are given the height as well as the base. We can use these values and plug them into the equal $\frac{b \cdot h}{2}$. If we do, we get the equation, $A = \frac{3 \cdot 4}{2}$. If we simplify this, we get that answer, $\boxed{A = 6 \text{ units}^2}$. □

Problem 291

Find the area of the triangle:

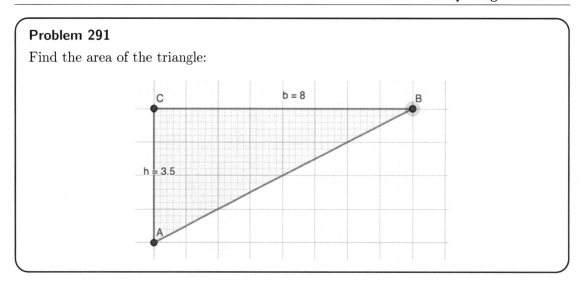

Proof. Looking at this problem, we notice although we say the area is base times the height, it doesn't mean that the base has to be at the bottom. The base of the triangle can be any sides other than the altitude. We know that values for the base and height, we can now plug them into the equation and solve for the area. if we do, we get the equation, $A = \frac{3.5 \cdot 8}{2}$. If we simplify this, we get the answer, $\boxed{A = 14 \text{ units}^2}$. $\qquad \square$

Problem 292

Find the height of the triangle:

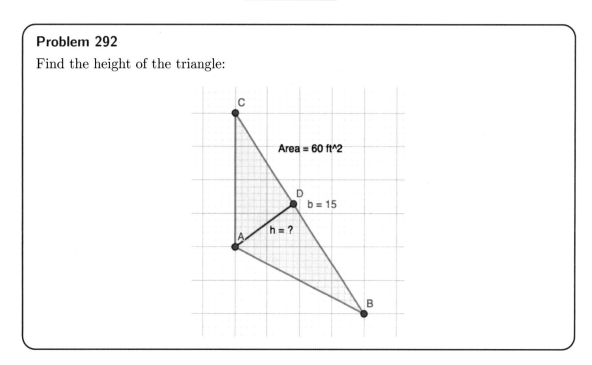

Proof. Unlike the last few problems, we now have the area of the shape and need to find the height. We can solve by plugging in the given values. If we do, then we get the equation, $60 = \frac{15 \cdot h}{2}$. We can ow solve for h. If we simplify the equation, we get $60 \cdot 2 = 15 \cdot h$. If we simplify this, we get that the height of the triangle is $\boxed{h = 8 \text{ feet}}$. □

Problem 293

Assuming that all the sides of the polygon are equal, find the area of the triangle:

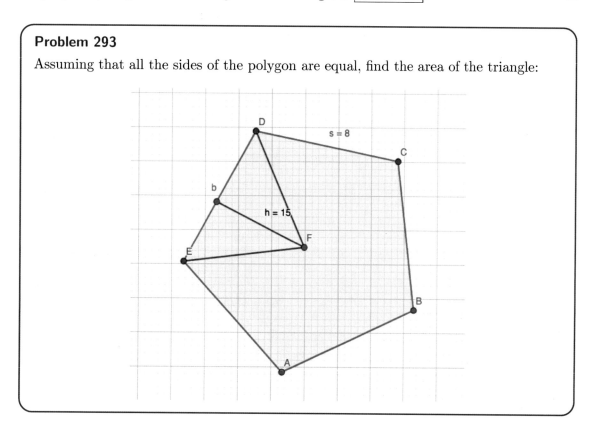

Proof. In this problem, we are given a 5 sided polygon with side length 8. Because all the sides are equal, we can see that b is also equal to 8. Using this information, we can plug them into the equation and find the area of the triangle. If we plug them into the equation, we get, $A = \frac{8 \cdot 15}{2}$. If we simplify this, we get that the area of the triangle is $\boxed{A = 60 \text{ units}^2}$. □

§56 Perimeter of Triangles

In this section, we will discuss a rather simple idea: Perimeter of Triangles. You have seen the Area of Triangles already. This is essentially just the amount of "space" inside the triangle. Now, we will explore the perimeter of a triangle.

Definition 56.1 (Perimeter of Triangles) — The perimeter of a triangle with side lengths

169

a, b, c is $a + b + c$.

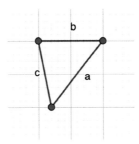

Let's try some examples.

Problem 294

Find the perimeter of the following triangle.

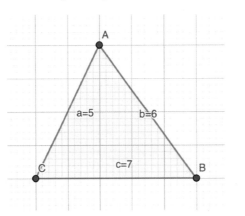

Problem 295

Find the perimeter of the triangle:

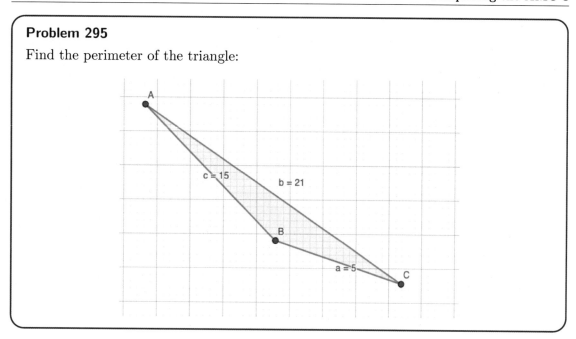

Proof. Finding the perimeter of a triangle is very simple. To do this, we just add up all the sides of the triangle and that is our perimeter. If we look at our triangle, we see the side lengths, 21, 15, and 5. If we add them up, we get that the perimeter of the triangle is $\boxed{P = 41 \text{ units}}$. $\qquad \square$

> **Remark 56.2.** Similar to the perimeter of a triangle, the perimeter of any polygon is simply the sum of its sides. For example, the area of a rectangle with w width and l length would be $P = w + l + w + l = 2(w + l)$.

§56.1 Perimeter of Triangles Problems

Problem 296

Find the perimeter and area of the following triangle given that $\angle ACB$ is a right angle.

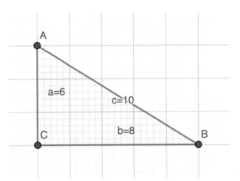

Problem 297

Farmer Joe trades his cows for some rope. He wants the rope to be the necessary length such that he is able to wrap the ropes around 3 points which are on his farm in the following way.

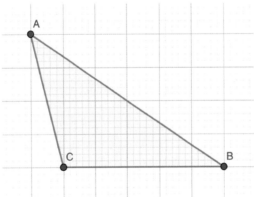

With his handy-dandy 6 inch ruler, he measured $\overline{AB}$ to be 100 feet, $\overline{BC}$ to be 50 feet, and $\overline{AC}$ to be 60 feet.

How much rope does he need (approximately) in feet? **Bonus Problem:** How many 6 inch measurements did he make? If he spent 10 seconds on lining up his ruler for each measurement, how long did this process take him? ☺

§57 Area of Polygons

§57.1 Area of Quadrilaterals

We have learned to find the area of a triangle, and now we will take this one step further by finding the area of different types of quadrilaterals.

> **Definition 57.1** (Quadrilateral) — A quadrilateral is a polygon with 4 sides.

Now that we have a (bit) more solid understanding of Geometry, let's revisit an important problem.

Problem 298

What is the sum of the angles in a triangle?

Proof. We start with an arbitrary triangle:

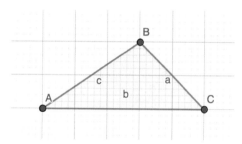

We draw a line parallel to (going in the same direction as) $\overline{AC}$ like so:

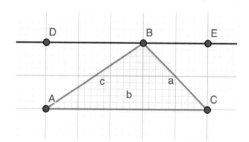

Because $\overline{AC}$ is parallel to $\overline{DE}$, we must have $\angle DBA = \angle BAC$ (take this upon faith for now) and $\angle BCA = \angle CBE$ (again, take this upon faith for now). Then,

$$\angle BAC + \angle BCA + \angle ABC = \angle ABD + \angle CBE + \angle ABC = 180°$$

because $\angle DBE$ is a straight angle. □

Now, we can find the sum of the angles in a quadrilateral.

Problem 299

What is the sum of the angles in a quadrilateral?

Proof. The proof for this is rather simple. We start with a generic quadrilateral:

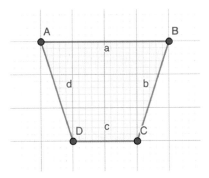

Then, we connect two opposite vertices, or points, on the quadrilateral, like so:

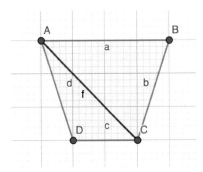

Now, the sum of the angles in the quadrilateral is equal to the sum of the angles in triangles $\triangle ABC$ and $\triangle ADC$. In each triangle, there are $180° + 180° = 360°$. Therefore, there are $360°$ in a quadrilateral. □

§57.2 Area of Squares

We start off with the definition of one of the most simple quadrilaterals:

Definition 57.2 (Square) — A square is a quadrilateral in which all of the sides have the same length and all four of the angles are right angles.

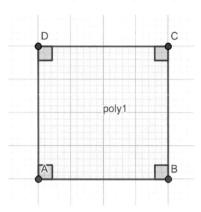

Let's practice finding the area of a square.

Problem 300

Find the area of the following square:

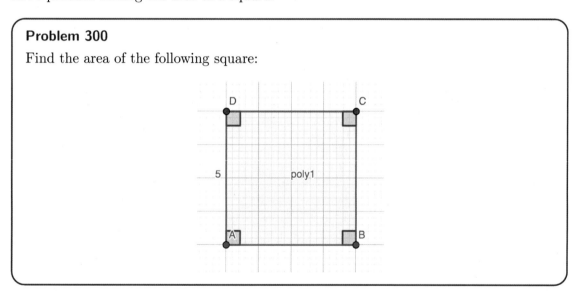

Proof. To find the area of a square, we can multiply its "width" by its "length". This means that we multiply 5 by 5. This is the same as

$$5 \text{ units} \times 5 \text{ units} = \boxed{25 \text{ units}^2}.$$

Remember, we have "units²" as our label and not "units" because we multiply "units" by itself in this computation. $\qquad\square$

This was rather simple concept that did not need a lot of thought. Let's expand this concept to rectangles.

§57.3 Area of Rectangles

Definition 57.3 (Rectangle) — A rectangle is a quadrilateral that has all right angles.

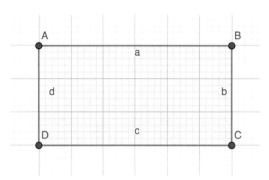

Remark 57.4. It quickly follows from this that $a = c$ and $b = d$ (take this upon faith for now). Then, we have two important/unique side lengths: a and b.

In our "derivation" for the area of a triangle, we eluded to the formula for the area of a rectangle. You may have also seen this in the Area of Squares section. Let's see how to find the area.

Problem 301

Find the area of the following rectangle:

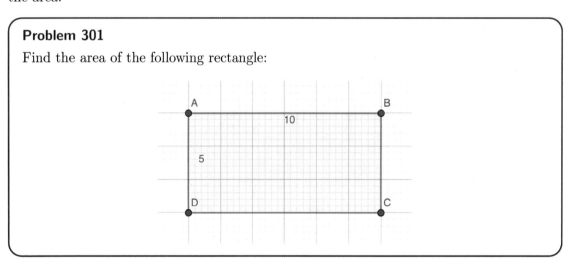

Proof. In order to find the area of a rectangle, we multiply its "width" by its "length" yet again, just like with squares. However, in squares we had that the width and the length were the same (by definition of a square). Now, the width and length are 5 and 10, respectively.

Remark 57.5. The length is often the larger side in a rectangle while the width is often the shorter side.

So, the area of the rectangle is

$$5 \text{ units} \times 10 \text{ units} = \boxed{50 \text{ units}^2}.$$

□

§57.3.1 Area of Squares and Rectangles Problems

Problem 302

Find the area of the following rectangle:

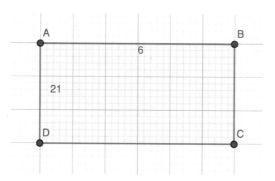

Problem 303

Find the area of the following rectangle:

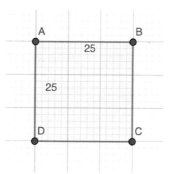

(Hint: This is a rectangle, but is this also a square? Hmm...)

Problem 304

We saw something interesting in the last problem. This ignites the questions:

1. Is every square a rectangle?

2. Is every rectangle a square?

(Hint: Try a few examples. The last two problems are good examples as well.)

Problem 305

Find the area of the following rectangle:

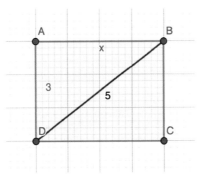

(Hint: Remember the Pythagorean Theorem. There are two steps here: 1) Finding the width and height, and 2) using these to find the area of the rectangle.)

§57.4 Area of Parallelograms

A parallelogram is another quadrilateral that is very similar to a square and a rectangle.

To define it, we must formally introduce a concept that we have informally used before.

Definition 57.6 (Parallel Lines) — Parallel lines are lines that go in the same direction.

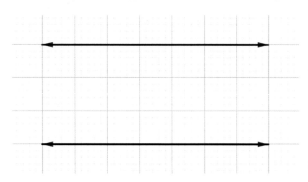

It quickly follows that if two lines are parallel, then they are either the same line or they never intersect. (Why?)

Definition 57.7 (Parallelogram) — A parallelogram is a quadrilateral with opposite sides that are parallel to each other.

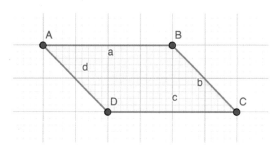

From this definition, we can find that the opposite side lengths of a parallelogram are equal. So, $a = c$ and $b = d$, just like in a rectangle.

Let us now find the area of a parallelogram.

Problem 306

Find the area of the given parallelogram. The parallelogram has been divided and you have been given a side that is perpendicular to the "base."

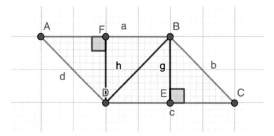

Proof. We split this problem in two, literally. We wish to find the area of $ABCD$, so we compute the area of $\triangle ABD$ and $\triangle CBD$ and add them to find the answer. (Why can we do this?)

Remark 57.8. Instead of saying "the area of $\triangle ABC$" or "the area of $ABCD$" we can simply say $[\triangle ABC]$ or $[ABCD]$. The brackets here mean "the area of."

We can find the $[\triangle ABD]$ by computing $\frac{a \cdot h}{2}$ by the formula for the area of a triangle.

Similarly, we can find the area of $[\triangle CBD]$ by computing $\frac{c \cdot g}{2}$.

We can find our answer by adding the two:

$$\frac{a \cdot h}{2} + \frac{c \cdot g}{2}.$$

However, we can simplify this. First, $a = c$ as mentioned earlier. Additionally, because $FBCD$ is a rectangle (why?), we also have that $h = g$. Then, we can rewrite the above expression using only a and h. We get

$$\frac{a \cdot h}{2} + \frac{a \cdot h}{2} = 2 \cdot \frac{a \cdot h}{2} = \boxed{a \cdot h}.$$

More generally, the area of a parallelogram is the product of its "base" and its "height," where the "height is the length of the segment perpendicular to the base between the base and its opposite side. (Make sure you understand what is happening here!) □

Remark 57.9 (Splitting a Quadrilateral into Two Triangles)**.** When computing the sum of the angles in a quadrilateral and in the last problem as well, we used a very important problem solving tool for quadrilaterals in general:

It is often helpful to split a quadrilateral into two triangles.

This trick is especially important when trying to find the area of a quadrilateral, as we did in the last problem.

§57.4.1 Area of Parallelograms Problems

Problem 307

Prove or disprove the following:

1. A rectangle is a parallelogram;

2. A parallelogram is a rectangle.

(Hint: Does a parallelogram need to have right angles?)

Problem 308

Find the area of the following parallelogram:

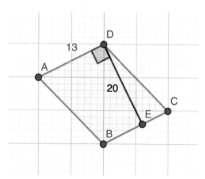

Problem 309

Find the area of the blue shaded region given that $ABCD$ is a parallelogram.

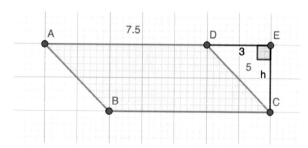

(Hint: Pythagorean Theorem.)

§57.5 Area of Rhombuses

A rhombus is another quadrilateral that is very similar to a square.

Definition 57.10 (Rhombus) — A rhombus is a quadrilateral whose sides are all the same length.

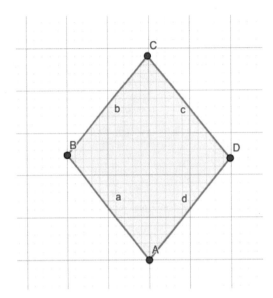

Using this image, let's look at how to solve for the area of the rhombus.

Problem 310

Find the area of the rhombus. The rhombus has been divided by its two diagonals.

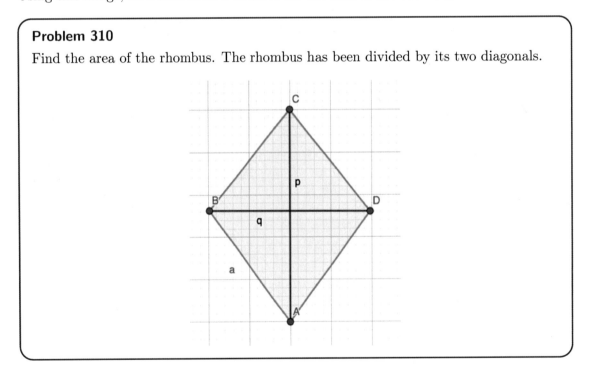

Proof. We split the rhombus into 4 parts by drawing the diagonals. To find the area of the rhombus, lets solve for each of the individual triangles' areas.

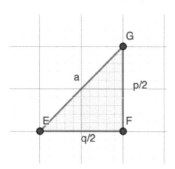

This image is one of the triangles once the rhombus is cut by the diagonals. Now, lets find its area. Because we know that the area of the triangle is base $\cdot$ base, we can use to find that the area of the triangle is $\frac{\frac{q}{2} \cdot \frac{p}{2}}{2}$. If we do that, we get $\frac{\frac{p \cdot q}{4}}{2}$, which simplifies to $\frac{p \cdot q}{8}$. That is the area of one triangle. Because we have 4 of those, we multiply it by 4. This gives us $\frac{p \cdot q}{8} \cdot 4$. If we simplify this, we get that the area of a rhombus is $\boxed{\dfrac{p \cdot q}{2}}$. □

Problem 311

Given the rhombus, find its area.

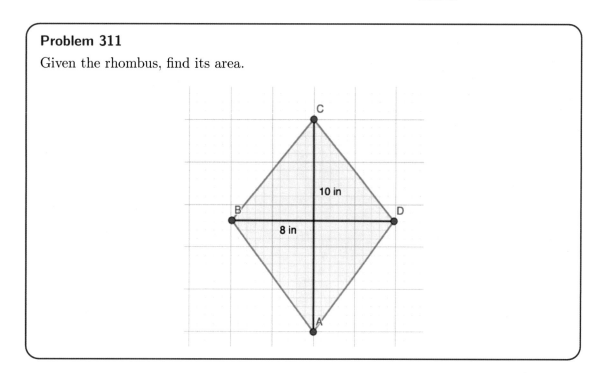

Proof. If we use the formula that we proved, we can find the area of the rhombus. We know that p is 10, q is 8 and c is 6. If we substitute the values, we get that the area is $A = \frac{10 \cdot 8}{2}$. If we simplify this, we get that the area of the rhombus is $\boxed{40 \text{ in}^2}$. □

§57.5.1 Area of Rhombus Problems

Problem 312

Given the rhombus, find its area.

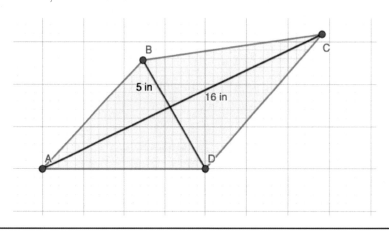

Problem 313

Given what you know about the area of a rhombus and Pythagorean triples, find the area of the shaded region.

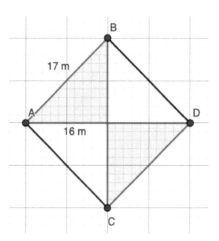

§57.6 Area of Trapezoids

Trapezoids are very similar to parallelograms, but not quite.

> **Definition 57.11** (Trapezoids) — A trapezoid is a quadrilateral in which there is one

pair of parallel sides. This means that two of the side lengths are parallel to each other.

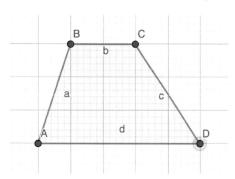

Remark 57.12. There is some discrepancy in the mathematics community as to whether a trapezoid has exactly one pair of parallel sides or at least one pair of parallel sides (meaning that it can have two sets of parallel sides, so it can be a parallelogram). Here, we will assume that a trapezoid has one pair of parallel sides.

Following the pattern from the last few sections, let us find the area of a trapezoid.

Problem 314

Find the area of the following trapezoid in terms of the given side lengths.

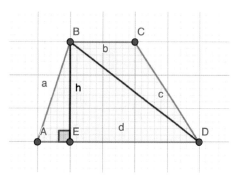

Proof. Similar to the way that we found the area of a parallelogram, let us find the area of a trapezoid by splitting our problem in half. We first calculate $[\triangle ABD]$ and then $[\triangle CDB]$ and finally we add these two together to get our answer. Make sure you understand this strategy as it can be applied to many area problems.

We can find $[\triangle ABD]$ easily by using the formula

$$\frac{\text{base} \cdot \text{height}}{2},$$

where the base is d and height is h. So, $[\triangle ABD] = \frac{d \cdot h}{2}$. Similarly, we have that $[\triangle CDB] = \frac{b \cdot h}{2}$ by the same formula (Why?). Then, we add these together to find the total area to be:

$$\frac{d \cdot h}{2} + \frac{b \cdot h}{2} = \boxed{\frac{1}{2} \cdot (b + d) \cdot h}.$$

Make sure you see how we find this through factoring out h.

> **Remark 57.13** (Bases and Height of a Trapezoid). Note that we say "bases of a trapezoid" when we talk about b and d. Additionally, the "height of a trapezoid" is h. Note that the height is perpendicular to both bases.

More generally, the area of a trapezoid is the average of the bases multiplied by the height of the trapezoid. $\square$

Let's try a problem to get the hang of this.

Problem 315

Find the area of the following trapezoid:

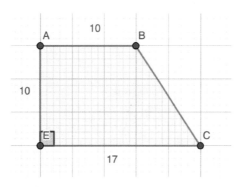

Proof. To find the area, we need:

1. The average of the bases;

2. The height of the trapezoid.

The average of the bases is just $\frac{10+17}{2} = 13.5$.

We also know that the height is a side connecting the two bases that is perpendicular to the two bases. Hey! Side $\overline{AE}$ of the trapezoid satisfies this condition. Does that mean that $\overline{AE}$ is the height as well? Yes, it does! (Think about it.) The height is then 10, as given.

Finally, we multiply the two to get 13.5 units $\cdot$ 10 units $= \boxed{135 \text{ units}^2}$. $\square$

§57.6.1 Area of Trapezoids Problems

Problem 316

Find the area of the following trapezoid:

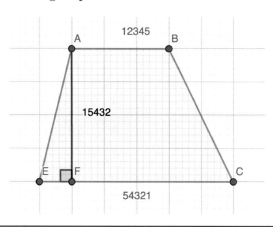

Problem 317 (AMC 8 2003: Problem 21)

The area of trapezoid $ABCD$ is 164 cm^2. The altitude is 8 cm, AB is 10 cm, and CD is 17 cm. What is BC, in centimeters?

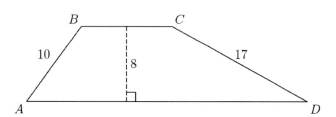

(Hint: Can you use the Pythagorean Theorem? Look for right angles!)

Problem 318 (Median of a Trapezoid)

The median of a trapezoid is a segment that is exactly in between (and parallel to) the bases. See if you can draw the median of a trapezoid.

Further, try to prove that the length of the median is the average of the bases. How can the length of the median be used with the height of the trapezoid to find the trapezoid's area?

§57.7 General Area of Polygons

When solving for the area of polygons, the general way to do it would be to split it up into multiple shapes. By doing that, you can find the area of each individual shape and add them together. Now, we will look at solving for the area of polygons by splitting up the shapes.

Problem 319

Given the polygon, find the area.

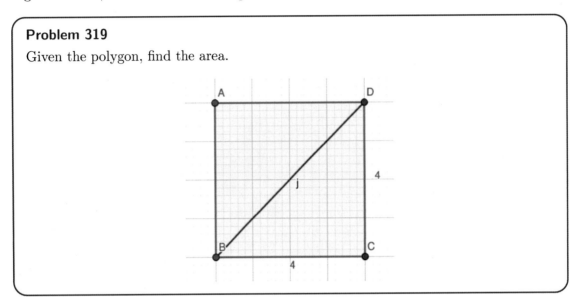

Proof. To solve this problem, we need to find the area of each individual triangle and add them up to find the total. Even though you can easily find the area using the equation for the area of a square, it is good practice to do this, because it will become easier when the shapes become more complicated. Now, let's find each individual area. We know that the shape is a square which means that all the sides will be equal. We can use that to find that the area of one triangle would be $\frac{4 \cdot 4}{2}$. This given us the area of one triangle is 8. Because we have two identical triangles, that means that the other triangles' area will also be 8. Using this knowledge, we can find that the area of the square is $\boxed{16 \text{ units}^2}$. □

Problem 320

Given the polygon, find the area.

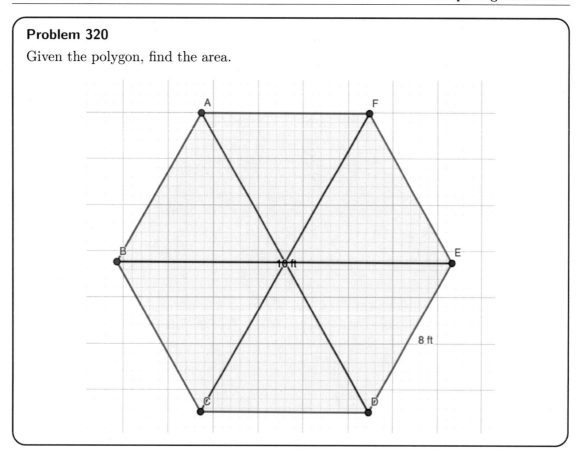

Proof. If we are given this problem, we have to first find the area of one triangle. Because it is a regular hexagon, all the sides are equal. To do this, looking at the image, we know that all the side lengths are 8 and that the diagonal lengths are 10. To find the area of one triangle, we can say that half the diagonal would be 5. If we redraw the polygon, but with one triangle, we would get this.

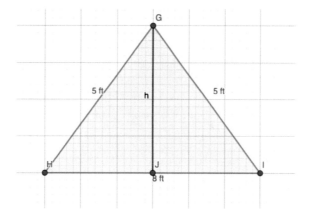

If we look at this image, we can see that the triangle is split into two equal triangles. If we split the base into two, we get the base for each individual triangle. Now, each side of the smaller triangles are found except for the height. We can now easily find the height of one of triangles by using the Pythagorean Theorem.

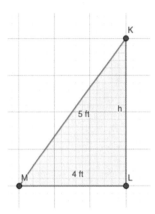

If we do, we get that the height of the triangle is 3 ft. We now know the height. Using this, we get solve for the overall triangle which is $\frac{3 \cdot 8}{2}$, giving is 12. Because we have 6 triangles in the polygon, we multiply this by 6. This gives us the answer us $\boxed{72 \text{ units}^2}$. $\qquad\square$

§58 Similar and Congruent Triangles

§58.1 Similar Triangles

In geometry, similar triangles are triangles that have the same shape and same angle measures, but different side lengths. You can only obtain the other similar triangle by uniformly scaling. Now, let's look at different cases of similar triangles.

Definition 58.1 (AA Similarity) — When two triangles are similar because of AA, it means that the angles are all equals. For future reference, when the similarity has an A, it stands for **angle**, and when there is an S, it stands for **side**. When all the angles are the same in both triangles, you can say that they are similar.

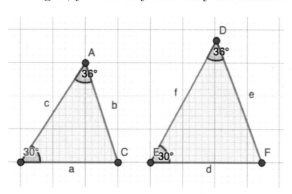

Let's try an example.

Problem 321

Find the length of the missing side.

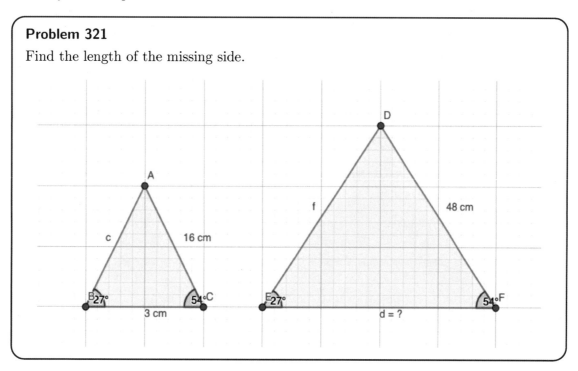

Proof. Before we solve this problem, we need to verify that it they are similar triangles. To do this, lets first look at the angles. We have to pairs of angles and each of them are equal. This is part of *AA* similarity which shows that they are similar. Because they are similar, we can solve for the missing side. To solve this problem, we need to find out by what we multiply each side by in the first triangle to get the corresponding side in the second triangle. Another name for this is the **Constant of Proportionality**. To find the constant of proportionality, we need to find out what we multiply 16 by to get 48. If we divide 48 by 16, we get the constant of proportionality is 3. We can use this constant of proportionality to find out that the missing side is $\boxed{9}$ ft. $\qquad\square$

Definition 58.2 (SAS Similarity) — When two triangles are similar because of SAS, it means that they are similar because of **side - angle - side**. This means that the two sides maintain a constant proportion with the other triangle and the angles in between are congruent.

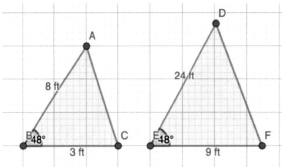

Now, let's try to solve a problem.

Problem 322

Find the length of the missing side length.

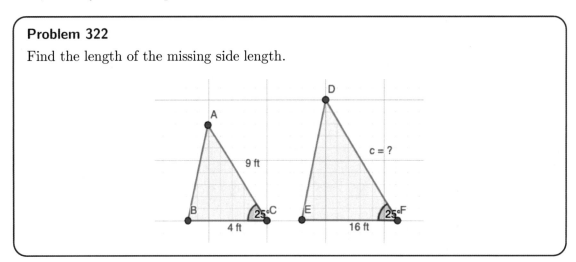

Proof. The way that you would solve this problem, is by first figuring out which similarity situation it is. If we look at the triangles, we see that we are given two sides and an angle in the middle. We can use that to find the constant of proportionality between the problems. If we look at the side with the length of 4 ft, we can see that the same side in the other triangle is 16 ft. This means that the constant of proportionality is 4 because $\frac{16}{4} = 4$. We can use that find that the other side is 9 ft, so then side c, would be $9 \cdot 4$, which gives us $\boxed{36\text{ft}}$. $\qquad\square$

Problem 323

Find the length of side FH.

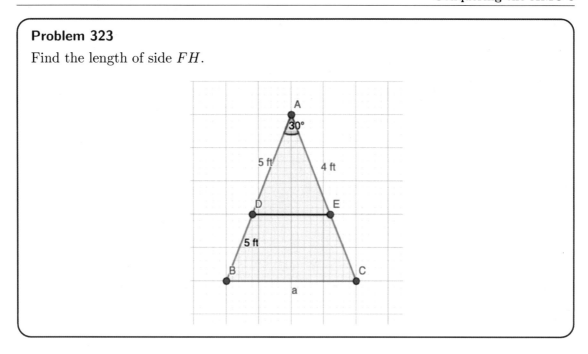

Proof. In this problem, we are given a triangle whose arrangement is slightly different than all the other examples that we had so far. To solve this problem we need to find out if the two triangles are similar are not first. To do that, let's find the missing angles. To do, we can look at the image,

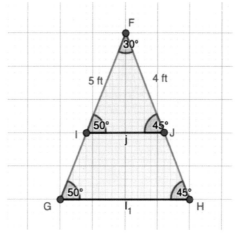

If you look at this image You can see that the ling segment IJ and GH are parallel. If those two lines are parallel, then the angles are on either side are equal to each like shown in the image. Now that we know this triangle has SAS similarity by looking at the triangle. Using this, we can solve for FH. We know that FG is 10 and FI is 5. You can see that the pattern is that we have to double the one of the split sides to find the value of the whole thing. We can use this to find that the length of $FH = FJ \cdot 2$. This means that we get that

$FH = \boxed{8\text{ft}}$. $\qquad\qquad\qquad\qquad\qquad\qquad\qquad\qquad\qquad\qquad\qquad$ $\square$

Definition 58.3 (SSS Similarity) — When two triangles are similar because of SSS, it means that all the sides in both triangles are similar. When I say similar, it means that they are all proportional to each other, through a constant term.

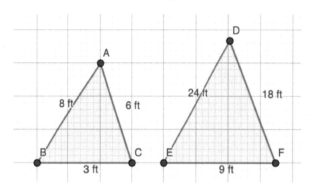

Problem 324

Given that:

1. $\overline{AB} = 10$;

2. $\overline{DE} = 5$;

3. $\overline{BC} = 15$;

4. $\overline{AC} = 8$;

5. $\overline{DF} = 4$;

6. $\triangle ABC \sim \triangle DEF$ (or $\triangle ABC$ is similar to $\triangle DEF$);

find $\overline{EF}$.

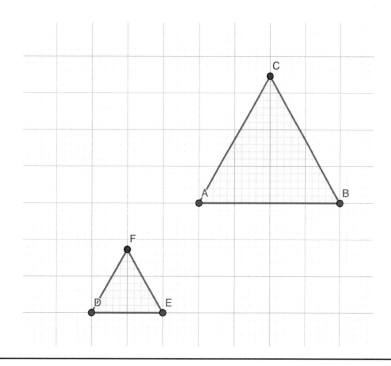

Proof. Because of the given similarity (6), we know that

$$\frac{\overline{AB}}{\overline{DE}} = \frac{\overline{BC}}{\overline{EF}} = \frac{\overline{AC}}{\overline{DF}}.$$

Be careful to note the sides that are similar to each other. Substituting the values that we know here, we find

$$\frac{10}{5} = \frac{15}{\overline{EF}} = \frac{8}{4} = 2$$

From this, we must have that

$$\frac{15}{\overline{EF}} = 2$$

or

$$\overline{EF} = \boxed{\dfrac{15}{2}}.$$

□

Note that we found our answer by first finding the constant of proportionality, which we found to be 2.

> **Definition 58.4** (ASA Similarity) — When two triangles are similar because of ASA, it means that they are similar because of **angle - side - angle**. What that means is that between in both triangles, both both pairs of angles are congruent to each other and the side in between those two angles are proportional through a constant term.

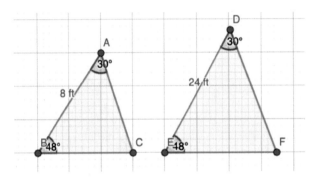

Problem 325

Find the length of the missing side.

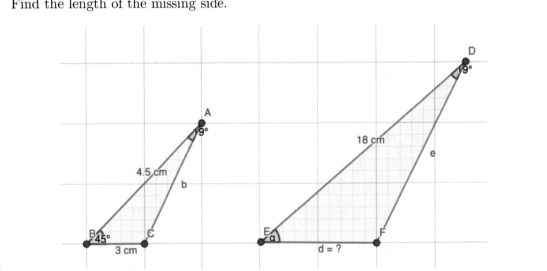

Proof. In this problem, before we start to find for the missing side, we need to confirm that the triangles are similar. To do this, we need to find out which similarity case this is. If we look at the triangle, we see that there are two angles and a side in between. Looking at this, it is clear that it is an example of ASA similarity. We now know that the two triangles are similar. With this, we can solve for the missing side. To solve for the missing side, we need to find the constant of proportionality. To do this, lets divide the known side in the larger triangle to its corresponding side in the smaller triangle. This means that we divide $\frac{18}{4.5} = 4$. We know that the constant of proportionality is 4. With this, we can solve for the missing side. If we do, we multiply by 3 by 4 to get $3 \cdot 4 = \boxed{12\text{cm}}$. $\square$

Definition 58.5 (AAS Similarity) — When two triangles are similar because of AAS, it means that they are similar because of **angle - angle - side**. This means that both pairs of angles are congruent, and the side adjacent to one of the angles is similar to same side on the other triangle.

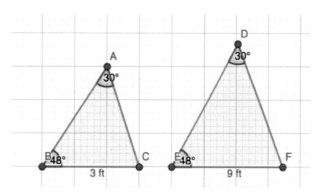

Problem 326

Given the triangles below, find x.

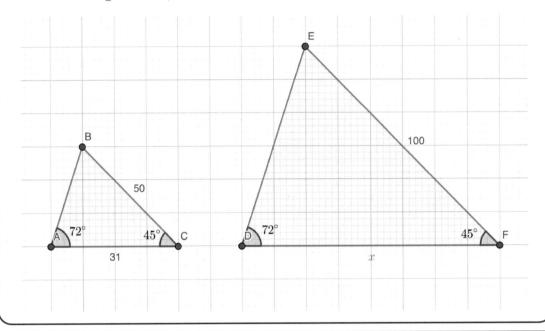

Conjecture 58.6

We conjecture that the triangles are similar. Specifically, we claim that $\triangle ABC \sim \triangle DEF$.

We know that this conjecture is true because:

Proof. $\frac{\overline{BC}}{\overline{EF}} = \frac{50}{100} = \frac{1}{2}$;

2. $\angle BAC = \angle EDF$;

3. $\angle ACB = \angle DFE$.

Note how we only needed the last two to prove that the triangles were similar, but the first gives us the constant of proportionality, which is 2.

Then, $x = 2 \cdot 31 = \boxed{62}$. $\qquad\square$

Definition 58.7 (HL Similarity) — When two triangles are similar because of HL, it means that they are similar because of **hypotenuse - leg**. It means that the hypotenuse of both triangles are similar as well as one of the legs. This can only be used right triangles.

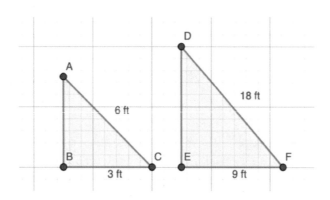

Problem 327

Find the length of the missing side.

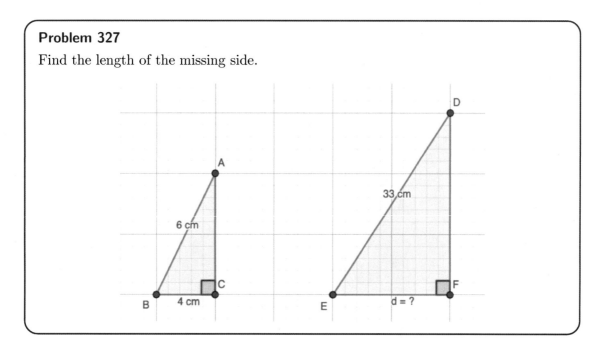

Proof. Before we start solving this problem, like all the other problems, we need to figure out if it the triangles are similar or not. If we look at the triangles, it is clear that they are right triangles. Taking this into consideration, the only similarity case which has a right triangle in it is HL similarity. Now that we have found out what kind of similarity is, we can solve for the missing sides. The thing we need to solve for the missing side would be the constant of proportionality. To find this, lets divide the hypotenuse on the larger triangle by its corresponding side on the smaller triangle. If we do this we get, $\frac{33}{6} = 5.5$. We now know that the constant of proportionality is 5.5. Using this, we can solve for the missing side on the larger triangle. If we do, we multiply 4 by 5.5 to get, $3 \cdot 5.5 = \boxed{16.5\text{cm}}$. $\qquad \square$

§58.2 Congruent Triangles

Unlike similar triangles, the conditions that need to be met to make it congruent are a bit different. These conditions are, the corresponding angles on the two triangles must be congruent and the corresponding sides on both triangles must also be congruent. This is the differences in similar triangles and congruent triangles. Now, lets look at the different cases of congruent

> **Definition 58.8** (AA Congruence) — When two triangles are congruent because of AA, it means that the angles are all equals. For future reference, when the similarity has an A, it stands for **angle**, and when there is an S, it stands for **side**. When all the angles are the same in both triangles, you can say that they are similar.

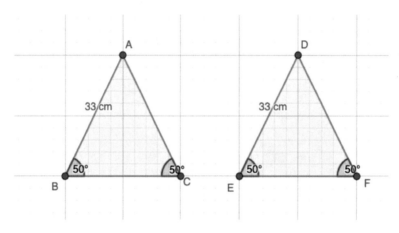

triangles.

Problem 328

Find the length of the missing side.

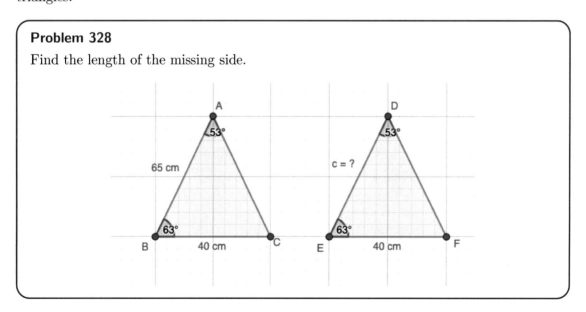

Proof. Before we solve this problem, we need to make sure that the two triangles are congruent. To do this, lets look at the angles and sides. The corresponding angles are congruent to each other and the pair of sides are also equal. This shows us that the two triangles are congruent through AA. Now, we can solve for the missing side. Because the constant of proportionality should be pairs of sides in order for the two triangles to be congruent, that also means that the missing side will be equal to its corresponding side in the other triangle. This means that the missing side has length $\boxed{65\text{cm}}$. $\square$

Definition 58.9 (SAS Congruence) — When two triangles are congruent because of SAS, it means that they are congruent because of **side - angle - side**. This means that the two sides maintain a constant proportion with the other triangle and the angles in between are congruent. This constant is 1.

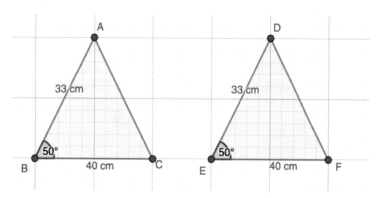

Problem 329

Find the length of the missing side.

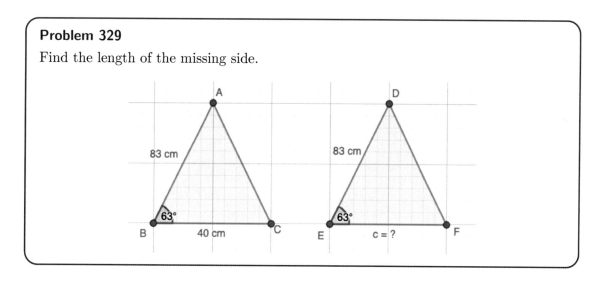

Proof. Before we solve for the missing side, we need to confirm whether or not the two triangles are congruent. Looking at the triangles, we notice that there is an angle in between two sides. This situation is SAS congruence. Now that we know that the two triangles are congruent, we can solve for the missing side. Because we know that the missing side is equal to the corresponding side in the other triangle, we can figure out that the length of the missing side is $\boxed{40\text{cm}}$. □

Definition 58.10 (SSS Congruence) — When two triangles are congruent because of *SSS*, it means that all the sides in both triangles are congruent. When I say congruent, it means that they are all proportional to each other, through a constant term. This constant term is 1.

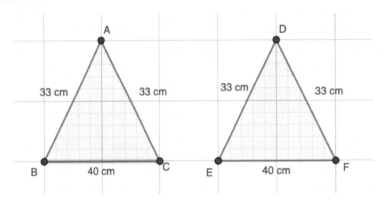

Problem 330

Find the length of the missing side.

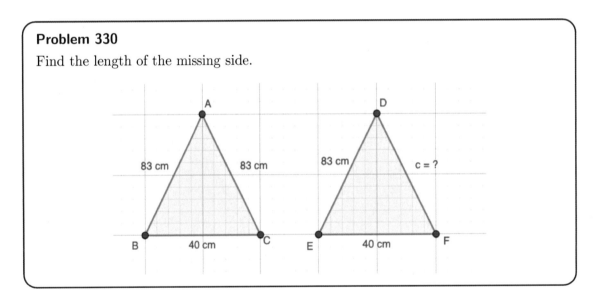

Proof. To solve this problem, we need to confirm that two triangles are congruent. If we look at all the sides, they are all equal. This shows us that the two triangles are congruent through *SSS*. We can now solve for the missing side. If we do, we get that the missing side should be equal to its corresponding side in the other triangle. That means that the missing side's length is $\boxed{83\text{cm}}$. □

Definition 58.11 (ASA Congruence) — When two triangles are congruent because of *ASA*, it means that they are congruent because of **angle - side - angle**. What that means is that between in both triangles, both both pairs of angles are congruent to each other and the side in between those two angles are proportional through a constant term. This constant term is 1.

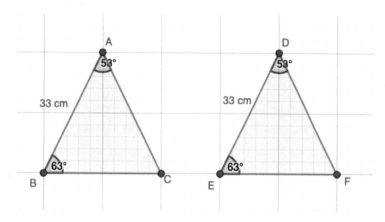

Problem 331

Find the length of the missing side.

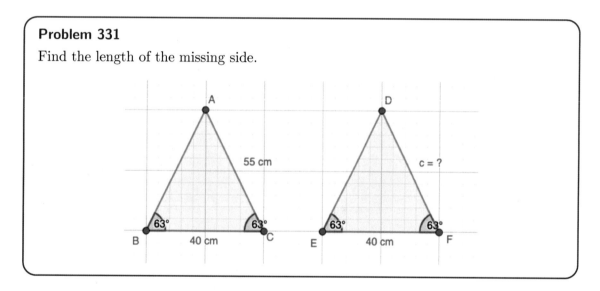

Proof. Before we solve this problem, we need to figure out whether the two triangles are congruent or not. To do that, we need to look at the sides. If we look at the first triangles, we have a side in between two angles. This situation is part of *ASA* congruence. Now that we know that the two triangles are congruent, we can solve for the missing side. To do this, we need to look at the missing side's corresponding side in the other triangle. If we do this, we can find out that the missing side. If we do this, we find out that the length of the missing side is $\boxed{55\text{cm}}$. □

Definition 58.12 (AAS Congruence) — When two triangles are congruent because of *AAS*, it means that they are congruent because of **angle - angle - side**. This means that both pairs of angles are congruent, and the side adjacent to one of the angles is congruent to same side on the other triangle.

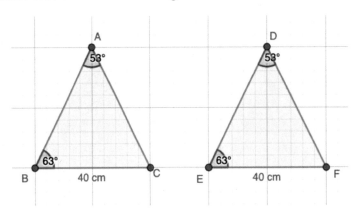

Problem 332

Find the length of the missing side.

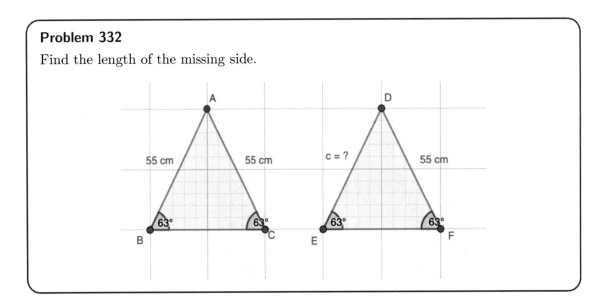

Proof. Before we start to solve the problem, we need to figure out whether the two triangles are congruent or not. To do this, lets look at the sides and angles. If we look at the angles, we have two angles, whose corresponding angles are congruent. Also, the lines are adjacent to one of the angles. This means that the two triangles are congruent through *AAS*. Now, we can start solving the problem. If we want to find the length of the missing side, we need to look at its corresponding side on the other triangle. The corresponding side has a length of 55 cm. This means that the length of the missing side will also be of length, $\boxed{55\text{cm}}$. □

Definition 58.13 (HL Congruence) — When two triangles are congruent because of HL, it means that they are congruent because of **hypotenuse - leg**. It means that the hypotenuse of both triangles are congruent as well as one of the legs. This can only be used right triangles.

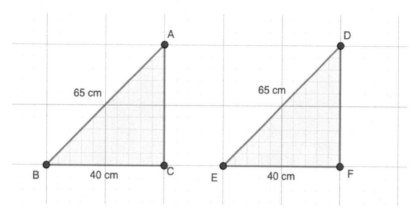

Problem 333

Find the length of the missing side.

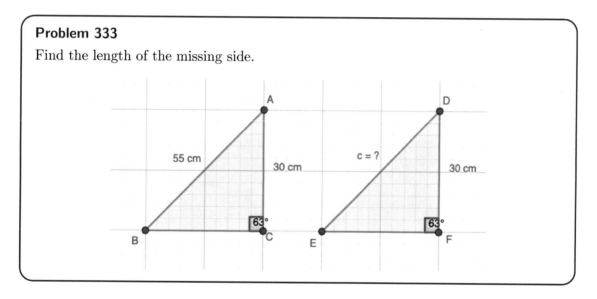

Proof. Before we start solving the problem, we need to make sure that the two triangles are congruent. Because this triangle is a right triangle, there is only one case where two right triangles are congruent and that is HL congruency. Now that we know that the two triangles are congruent, we can solve for the missing side. To solve for the missing side, we need to find the length of its corresponding side in the other triangle. If we do this, we get that the length of the missing side is $\boxed{55\text{cm}}$. □

§58.3 Similar and Congruent Triangles Problems

Problem 334 (AMC 8 2002: Problem 20)

The area of triangle XYZ is 8 square inches. Points A and B are midpoints of congruent segments $\overline{XY}$ and $\overline{XZ}$. Altitude $\overline{XC}$ bisects $\overline{YZ}$. The area (in square inches) of the shaded region is?

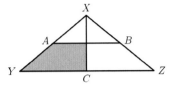

Problem 335 (AMC 8 2006: Problem 19)

Triangle ABC is an isosceles triangle with $\overline{AB} = \overline{BC}$. Point D is the midpoint of both $\overline{BC}$ and $\overline{AE}$, and $\overline{CE}$ is 11 units long. Triangle ABD is congruent to triangle ECD. What is the length of $\overline{BD}$?

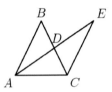

Problem 336 (AMC 8 2007: Problem 23)

What is the area of the shaded part shown in the 5 x 5 grid?

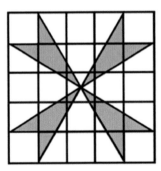

(Note: This is an area problem as well. Hint: What is the area of the non-shaded region?)

Problem 337 (AMC 8 2008: Problem 23)

In square $ABCE$, $AF = 2FE$ and $CD = 2DE$. What is the ratio of the area of $\triangle BFD$ to the area of square $ABCE$?

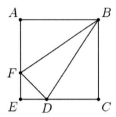

(Hint: Name some side lengths. Assign some variables!)

§59 Circles

We now transition to one of the most prevalent topics in Geometry (besides triangles) on the AMC 8. We start with a formal definition of a circle.

Definition 59.1 (Circle) — A circle is the locus of points (or the set of all points) that are a certain distance r from a point O. The length r is called the radius of the circle and O is the center.

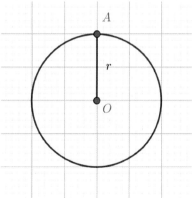

In the above circle, point A is one of the points on the circle. We often refer to a circle with center O as simply circle O.

We call $d = 2r$ the diameter of a circle. This is the distance between any two points that are on opposite sides of a circle.

Remark 59.2. A circle is not a polygon because it is curved.

Similar to the triangle sections, let us explore the "perimeter" and area of a circle.

§59.1 Circumference

First, we look at the "perimeter" of a circle. This is the length of the curved side that goes all the way around the circle. We commonly call this the circumference of a circle.

Definition 59.3 (Circumference) — The circumference of a circle is the length of the side of the circle. In other words, if we unwrapped the circle into a line segment, the circumference is the length of this line segment.

This is a bit harder to find, mainly because the side is curved.

We can get some intuition around this, thinking about the different factors that affect the circumference of a circle. A circle is uniquely defined by its center and radius, so it would make sense for the length of the circumference to depend on the radius (the only side length that determines a circle).

In fact, there exists a constant π such that if C is the circumference and r is the radius, then

$$C = 2\pi r.$$

Since $d = 2r$, we also have that

$$C = \pi d.$$

Rearranging this, we get

$$\pi = \frac{C}{d},$$

meaning that π is the ratio of a circle's circumference to its diameter. It turns out that we can calculate π to be about

$$3.14159265358979323846\ldots$$

In fact, π keeps on going on forever as it is irrational. We often just use $\pi \equiv 3.14$ or $\frac{22}{7} \equiv 3.142857\ldots$ as an estimation. However, it is helpful to know up to 3.14159.

Remark 59.4 (Pi Digits Contest). People memorize thousands of digits of π because it is such an important constant. I know about 80 digits of π at the time of writing this. Can you beat me?

Remark 59.5. Contests such as the AMC 8 will often ask you to leave your answer in terms of π rather than approximate it in order to have an "exact answer."

Let's try a few examples for finding the circumference of a circle.

Problem 338

Find the circumference of the following circle.

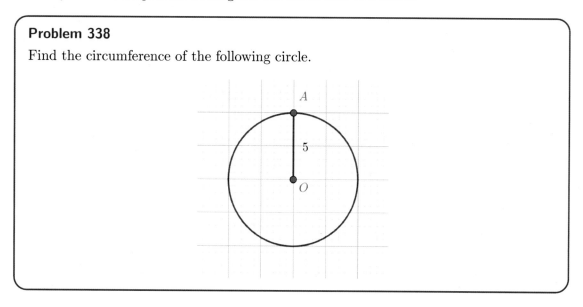

Proof. The radius of this circle is 5. Then, the circumference is $2\pi \cdot 5 = \boxed{10\pi \text{ units}}$.

Since 5 is the radius, $5 \cdot 2 = 10$ is the diameter and we can use $C = \pi d$ to find that $C = \pi \cdot 10 = \boxed{10\pi \text{ units}}$.

Remark 59.6. We often write 10π instead of $\pi 10$. This is not a hard and fast rule, just a tradition. ☺

□

This is a rather simple concept as we simply use a formula. Let's try one more.

Problem 339

Find the circumference of the following circle given the length of $\overline{AB}$, a diameter of circle O.

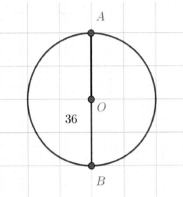

Proof. This time, we are not given the radius. Rather, we are given the diameter. We can use the formula $C = \pi d$ to find that the circumference is $C = \pi \cdot 36 = \boxed{36\pi \text{ units}}$.

We could have also found the radius and then used that to find the circumference. The radius is $\frac{36}{2} = 18$. Then, $C = 2\pi r = 2\pi \cdot 18 = \boxed{36\pi \text{ units}}$. This method is often more work than we need to do, but we include it here to make sure that you can easily convert between using the diameter and radius to find the circumference. $\square$

§59.2 Area

The area of a circle refers to the space inside. Unlike the circumference of the circle, the equation for the area is a bit different.

> Definition 59.7 — In geometry, the area of the circle is the area of the enclosed space.

To solve for the area of a circle, we need to the radius of the circle. We use the equation, $A = \pi r^2$. Using this, lets solve some problems.

Problem 340

Find the area of the circle.

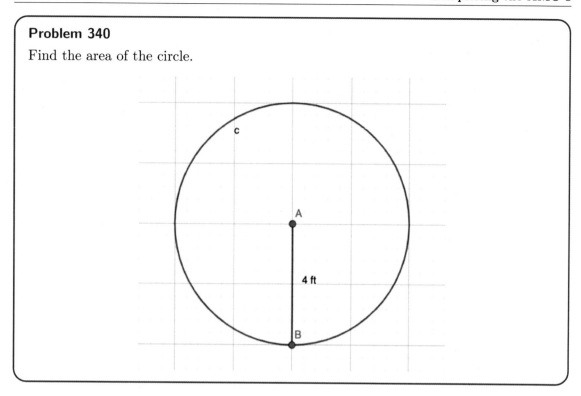

Proof. To solve this problem, we need to use the equation for the area of a circle. We know that the equation for the area of a circle is $A = \pi r^2$. To solve for the area, all we need to do is plug in the necessary values. We know that radius is 4 from the image. If we plug this into the equation, we get $A = \pi 4^2$. If we simplify this, we get that the area of the circle is $\boxed{A = 16\pi \text{ feet}^2}$. $\square$

Problem 341

Find the area of the circle.

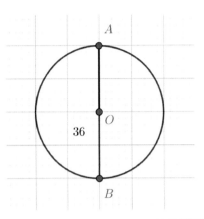

Proof. To solve this problem, we can again use the area of the circle, but we have a problem. In the formula, we require the radius but we are given the diameter in the picture. How do we find the radius? Well, we know that the diameter is twice the radius, which means that the radius will be the $\frac{\text{diameter}}{2}$, which gives us a radius of 18. We can now plug this into the equation and find that the area of the circle is $A = \pi 18^2$. If we simplify this, we get that the area of the circle is $\boxed{A = 324\pi \text{ units}^2}$ ◻

Problem 342

The area of a circle with radius r is $A = \pi r^2$. Let d be the diameter of the same circle. Find A in terms of d.

Proof. This problem becomes rather simple when we substitute $d = 2r$. (Recall that the diameter is twice the length of the radius.) We can rewrite this as $r = \frac{d}{2}$. Then, we know that

$$A = \pi r^2.$$

We can substitute $\frac{d}{2}$ in for r to find that

$$A = \pi r^2 = \pi \left(\frac{d}{2}\right)^2 = \pi \frac{d^2}{4}.$$

Therefore,

$$\boxed{A = \pi \frac{d^2}{4}}.$$

◻

212

§59.3 Sectors

In circles, we often wish to look at only a half circle, or a quarter circle. In this section, we look at how to find the area and circumference of sectors.

Problem 343

Find the area of the following sector.

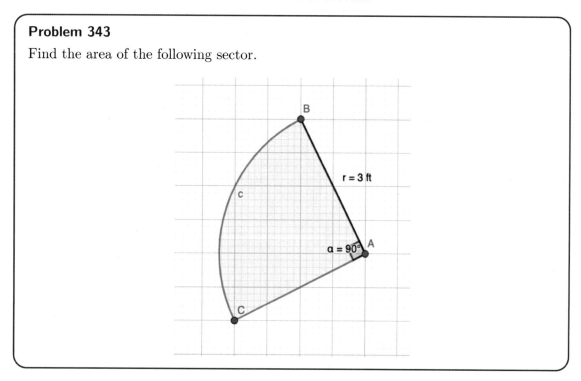

Proof. Let's start by finding the area of the whole circle. The area of this circle is $\pi \cdot 4^2 = 16\pi$ units^2. However, we **do not want** the area of the whole circle. Rather, we can the area of a portion, or a "sector" of the circle.

The total number of degrees in a circle is 360, by the definition of degrees. In this problem, however, we want the area of the circle bounded by only 60°.

This means that we only want $\frac{60°}{360°} = \frac{1}{6}$ of the circle's area. So, we can simply multiply the area of the circle by $\frac{1}{6}$ to find our answer. We get

$$16\pi \text{ units}^2 \cdot \frac{1}{6} = \frac{16}{6}\pi \text{ units}^2 = \boxed{\frac{8}{3}\pi \text{ units}^2}.$$

Make sure you see why and how we took only a portion of the area of the circle. □

Problem 344

Find the area of the following sector.

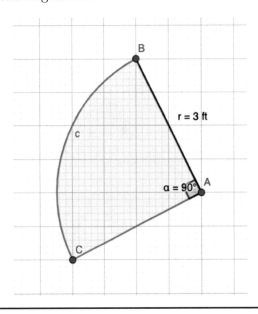

Proof. Before we start to solve for the area, we need to know what the equation for a sector is. The equation for a sector is $A = \frac{\theta}{360}\pi r^2$. If we look at the image, we have all the information needed to solve for the area. We have the sector's angle measure, which is $90°$, and the length of the radius, which is 3 feet. Using this, lets plug it into the equation. If we do, we get $A = \frac{90°}{360°}\pi 3^2$. We can simplify this to $A = \boxed{\frac{9}{4}\pi}$. $\qquad\square$

Problem 345

Find the circumference of the sector.

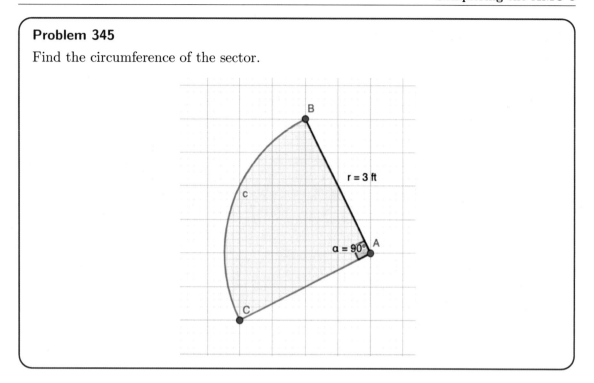

Proof. Before we start solving for the circumference, we need to know what the equation is. The equation for the circumference of a sector is $C = 2r \cdot (\frac{\theta}{360} \cdot 2\pi r)$. Now that we know the equation, we can solve for the circumference. If we do, we get that the circumference of the sector is $A = 2(3) \cdot (\frac{90}{360} \cdot 6\pi)$. If we simplify this, we get that the circumference is $C = \boxed{9\pi \text{ feet}}$. $\qquad\square$

Essentially, the pattern here is that we first find the total area or circumference of the circle. Then, we take a portion of this depending on the size of the sector.

§60 Geometry Problems

Here, we compiled a list of Geometry problems from the AMC 8. These are in no particular order. Using the skills you learned here as well as some active intuition, you should be able to solve all of these problems.

Problem 346 (AMC 8 1999: Problem 2)

What is the degree measure of the smaller angle formed by the hands of a clock at 10 o clock?

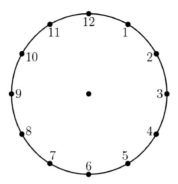

Problem 347 (AMC 8 1999: Problem 5)

A rectangular garden 60 feet long and 20 feet wide is enclosed by a fence. To make the garden larger, while using the same fence, its shape is changed to a square. By how many square feet does this enlarge the garden?

Problem 348 (AMC 8 1999: Problem 14)

In trapezoid $ABCD$, the sides AB and CD are equal. The perimeter of $ABCD$ is?

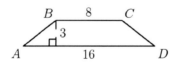

Problem 349 (AMC 8 1999: Problem 21)

The degree measure of angle A is?

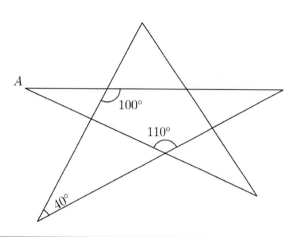

Problem 350 (AMC 8 1999: Problem 23)

Square $ABCD$ has sides of length 3. Segments CM and CN divide the square's area into three equal parts. How long is segment CM?

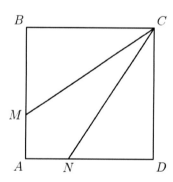

Problem 351 (AMC 8 1999: Problem 25)

Points B, D, and J are midpoints of the sides of right triangle ACG. Points K, E, I are midpoints of the sides of triangle JDG, etc. If the dividing and shading process is done 100 times (the first three are shown) and $AC = CG = 6$, then the total area of the shaded triangles is nearest?

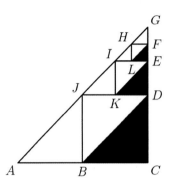

Problem 352 (AMC 8 2000: Problem 6)

Figure $ABCD$ is a square. Inside this square three smaller squares are drawn with the side lengths as labeled. The area of the shaded L-shaped region is?

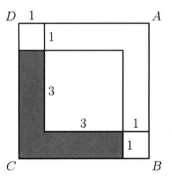

Problem 353 (AMC 8 2000: Problem 13)

In triangle CAT, we have $\angle ACT = \angle ATC$ and $\angle CAT = 36°$. If $\overline{TR}$ bisects $\angle ATC$, then $\angle CRT =$?

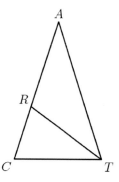

Problem 354 (AMC 8 2000: Problem 15)

Triangles ABC, ADE, and EFG are all equilateral. Points D and G are midpoints of $\overline{AC}$ and $\overline{AE}$, respectively. If $AB = 4$, what is the perimeter of figure $ABCDEFG$?

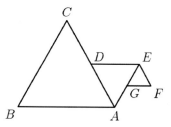

Problem 355 (AMC 8 2000: Problem 19)

Three circular arcs of radius 5 units bound the region shown. Arcs AB and AD are quarter-circles, and arc BCD is a semicircle. What is the area, in square units, of the region?

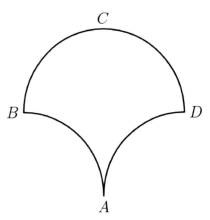

Problem 356 (AMC 8 2000: Problem 24)

If $\angle A = 20°$ and $\angle AFG = \angle AGF$, then $\angle B + \angle D =$

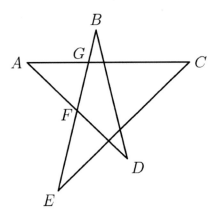

Problem 357 (AMC 8 2000: Problem 25)

The area of rectangle $ABCD$ is 72. If point A and the midpoints of $\overline{BC}$ and $\overline{CD}$ are joined to form a triangle, the area of that triangle is

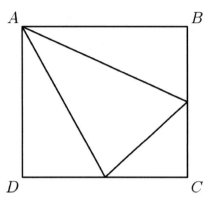

Problem 358 (AMC 8 2002: Problem 16)

Right isosceles triangles are constructed on the sides of a 3-4-5 right triangle, as shown. A capital letter represents the area of each triangle. Which one of the following is true?

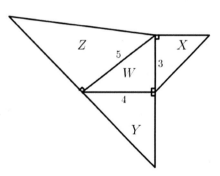

(A) $X + Z = W + Y$ (B) $W + X = Z$ (C) $3X + 4Y = 5Z$

(D) $X + W = \frac{1}{2}(Y + Z)$ (E) $X + Y = Z$

Problem 359 (AMC 8 2003: Problem 6)

Given the areas of the three squares in the figure, what is the area of the interior triangle?

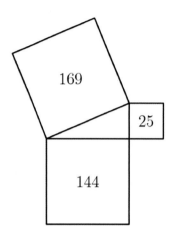

Problem 360 (AMC 8 2003: Problem 22)

The following figures are composed of squares and circles. Which figure has a shaded region with largest area?

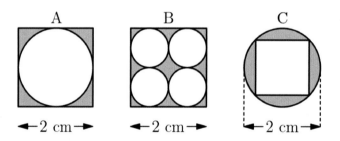

(**A**) A only   (**B**) B only   (**C**) C only   (**D**) both A and B   (**E**) all are equal

Problem 361 (AMC 8 2003: Problem 24)

A ship travels from point A to point B along a semicircular path, centered at Island X. Then it travels along a straight path from B to C. Which of these graphs best shows the ship's distance from Island X as it moves along its course?

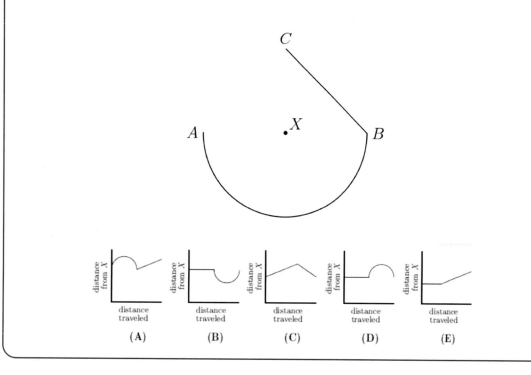

Problem 362 (AMC 8 2003: Problem 25)

In the figure, the area of square $WXYZ$ is 25 cm^2. The four smaller squares have sides 1 cm long, either parallel to or coinciding with the sides of the large square. In $\triangle ABC$, $AB = AC$, and when $\triangle ABC$ is folded over side $\overline{BC}$, point A coincides with O, the center of square $WXYZ$. What is the area of $\triangle ABC$, in square centimeters?

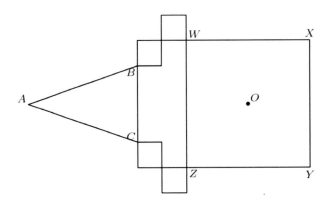

Problem 363 (AMC 8 2004: Problem 24)

In the figure, $ABCD$ is a rectangle and $EFGH$ is a parallelogram. Using the measurements given in the figure, what is the length d of the segment that is perpendicular to $\overline{HE}$ and $\overline{FG}$?

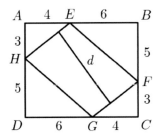

Problem 364 (AMC 8 2004: Problem 25)

Two 4×4 squares intersect at right angles, bisecting their intersecting sides, as shown. The circle's diameter is the segment between the two points of intersection. What is the area of the shaded region created by removing the circle from the squares?

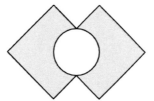

Problem 365 (AMC 8 2004: Problem 25)

A square and a triangle have equal perimeters. The lengths of the three sides of the triangle are 6.1 cm, 8.2 cm and 9.7 cm. What is the area of the square in square centimeters?

Problem 366 (AMC 8 2005: Problem 9)

In quadrilateral $ABCD$, sides $\overline{AB}$ and $\overline{BC}$ both have length 10, sides $\overline{CD}$ and $\overline{DA}$ both have length 17, and the measure of angle ADC is $60°$. What is the length of diagonal $\overline{AC}$?

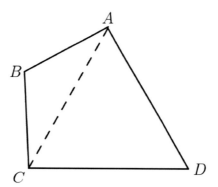

(Hint: Look for special triangles!)

Problem 367 (AMC 8 2005: Problem 13)

The area of polygon $ABCDEF$ is 52 with $AB = 8$, $BC = 9$ and $FA = 5$. What is $DE + EF$?

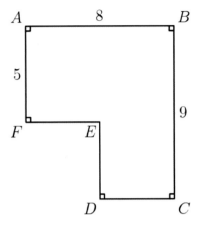

Problem 368 (AMC 8 2005: Problem 19)

What is the perimeter of trapezoid $ABCD$?

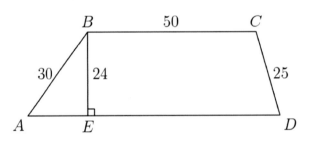

Problem 369 (AMC 8 2005: Problem 23)

Isosceles right triangle ABC encloses a semicircle of area 2π. The circle has its center O on hypotenuse $\overline{AB}$ and is tangent to sides $\overline{AC}$ and $\overline{BC}$. What is the area of triangle ABC?

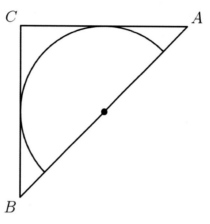

Problem 370 (AMC 8 2005: Problem 25)

A square with side length 2 and a circle share the same center. The total area of the regions that are inside the circle and outside the square is equal to the total area of the regions that are outside the circle and inside the square. What is the radius of the circle?

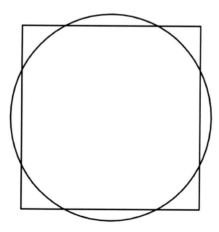

Part VII
Advanced Competition Tricks for the AMC 8

Conquering the AMC 8

§61 Introduction

Here, we will talk about Competition Tips and Tricks that can help make you faster. This is critical on math competitions such as the AMC 8 where you are timed to complete the test.

§62 Mental Math and Computation Tricks

A heap of the AMC 8 is computation. In this section, we will focus on some tricks that will help you increase the efficiency of your computations in order to help you fly past problems.

§62.1 Summing Large Numbers

Summing large numbers is often difficult, but it becomes easier if we break down these sums.

> **Problem 371**
> Compute: $644 + 996$.

Proof. This is a mouthful, so we start by first writing these numbers in terms of numbers that are relatively easier to add.

Specifically, we know that
$$644 = 640 + 4$$
and
$$996 = 1000 - 4.$$
So, when we compute the sum, we get
$$644 + 99 = 640 + 4 + 1000 - 4 = 640 + 1000 = \boxed{1640}.$$

$\square$

Let's try another example.

> **Problem 372**
> Compute: $625 + 175$.

Proof. We present two solutions:

Solution 1   We notice that
$$625 = 600 + 25$$
and
$$175 = 200 - 25.$$
Then,
$$625 + 175 = 600 + 25 + 200 - 25 = 600 + 200 = \boxed{800}.$$

Solution 2   If you're observant, you will notice that both of our numbers are divisible by 25.

Specifically,
$$625 = 25 \times 25$$
and
$$175 = 7 \times 25.$$
Then,
$$625 + 175 = 25 \times 25 + 7 \times 25 = (25 + 7) \times 25 = 32 \times 25 = \boxed{800}.$$

Notice how we used factoring to our advantage here. $\square$

§62.2 Multiplication Tricks

§62.2.1 Multiplication by 10

Multiplication by 10 is very simple. All we do is add a 0 at the end of the other number. For example:

> **Problem 373** (Multiplication by 10)
> Compute: 12345×10.

Proof. We simply add 0 to the end of 12345 to get $\boxed{123450}$. We can do this for multiplication by 10 in general. $\square$

If we have a decimal number, however, we move the decimal point one place to the right.

> **Problem 374**
> Compute: 12.53×10.

Proof. We move the decimal point one place to the right to get $\boxed{125.3}$. $\square$

§62.2.2 Multiplication by 5

Let's multiply a number x by 5. We get $5x$. Since $5 = \frac{10}{2}$, we can write this as

$$5x = \frac{10}{2}x = 10 \cdot \frac{x}{2}.$$

In other words, we can multiply a number by 5 by first dividing the number by 2 before multiplying by 10.

Let's try some examples.

Problem 375 (Multiplication by 5)

Compute: 12×5.

Proof. Some of you may know that the answer is $\boxed{60}$, but we will not use this simply because we wish to explain the concept of multiplication by 5. First, we divide 12 by 2 to get $\frac{12}{2} = 6$. Now, we multiply by 10, or add a 0, to get our answer $\boxed{60}$. $\qquad\square$

Problem 376

Compute: 13×5.

Proof. Again, some of you may know that the answer is $\boxed{65}$, but we will use the proposed method to find the answer. First, we divide 13 by 2 to get $\frac{13}{2} = 6.5$. Then, we multiply by 10, or move the decimal one place to the right to get $\boxed{65}$. $\qquad\square$

§62.2.3 Multiplication of a Two Digit Number by 11

This is easily explained through an example.

Problem 377

Compute: 52×11.

Proof. In order to multiply a two digit number by 11, we first add the digits of the number. Here, the sum of the digits is $5 + 2 = 7$. Then, our answer is

5 blank 2,

where 5 and 2 come from the original number 52. In the **blank** spot, we put the sum of the digits, which we had calculated as 7. Then, the answer is $\boxed{572}$. (Try to prove this method yourself! Hint: Try a few examples of long multiplication of numbers by 11.) $\qquad\square$

Let's see how this works in general.

Problem 378 (Multiplication by 11)

Let ab be a two digit number such that a is the tens digit and b is the units digit. (We are not doing $a \cdot b$!)

Compute: $ab \times 11$.

Proof. Just like before, we first find the sum of the digits. This is $a + b$.

Then, our answer is

$$a \textbf{ blank } b,$$

where a and b come from the given number ab. The number in the **blank** spot is the sum of the digits, or $a + b$. So, our answer is

$$\boxed{a(a+b)b},$$

where a is the hundreds digit, $a + b$ is the tens digit, and b is the units digit. $\square$

Let's try a small corner case.

Problem 379

Compute: 57×11.

Proof. The sum of the digits is $5 + 7 = 12$. However, this cannot be one of the digits! Just like in normal multiplication, we carry this over to the hundreds digit.

The hundreds digit was supposed to be 5, but now it is $5 + 1 = 6$ because of the carry over. Then, the middle digit is 2 (because we carried over the 1) and the units digit is 7, like normal. So, our answer is $\boxed{627}$. $\square$

§62.2.4 Two Digit Multiplication Trick 1

This next trick applies to two digit multiplication.

Let ab be a two digit number such that a is the tens digit and b is the units digit. Let ac be a two digit number such that a is the tens digit (yes, the same a as in the last number) and c is the units digit. We must also have that $b + c = 10$

We can compute the product $ab \times ac$ by computing the following:

1. $a \times (a + 1)$;

232

2. $b \times c$.

If $b \times c$ is a one digit number, then "convert" it to a one digit number by adding a zero to the beginning of it. For example, 9 becomes 09. Then, "concatenate," or put together, the answers for (1) and (2).

To clarify this process, let's try an example.

Problem 380

Compute: 37×33.

Proof. Firstly, we know that we can apply our trick here because the tens digit is the same and because the sum of the units digits is $7 + 3 = 10$. We compute both of the following as explained earlier:

1. $3 \times (3 + 1) = 3 \times 4 = 12$;

2. $7 \times 3 = 21$.

We then put these two together to get

$$12 \quad 21 = \boxed{1221}.$$

Note that if the product of the units digits was something like 9, then we would add a 0 in front to get 09 before we put the two answers together to get 12 09 = 1209. $\square$

§62.2.5 Two Digit Multiplication Trick 2

What if our numbers do not satisfy the requirements for Two Digit Multiplication Trick 1?

There is indeed a way to do two digit multiplication faster. Say we have two numbers ab and cd, where a and c are the tens digits and b and d are the units digits. Then, we first compute each of the following:

1. $b \cdot d$; The units digit of this answer is the units digit of the answer we carry over to the tens digit if necessary;

2. $a \cdot d + b \cdot c$; The units digit of this answer is the tens digit of the answer. Remember to add any carry overs from the units digit and to carry over to the hundreds digit if necessary;

3. $a \cdot c$; Add any carry overs and this answer contains the first few digits of your answer.

Let's try an example to clarify what this means.

233

> **Problem 381** (Two Digit Multiplication Trick 2)
> Compute: 13×24.

Proof. We write our problem again:
$$13 \times 24.$$

We first compute the product of the units digits, which is
$$3 \times 4 = 12.$$

This is a two digit number, so we carry the 1. We now know that the **units digit** of our answer is 2.

Now, we compute the product of the tens digit of one of the numbers and the tens digit of the other number. Specifically, we do
$$1 \times 4 + 3 \times 2 = 4 + 6 = 10.$$

We then add the carry over from the units digit to get $10 + 1 = 11$. Now, we know that 1 is the **tens digit** of our answer. We also carry over the 1 in the tens place to the hundreds digit.

To compute the hundreds digit, we simply compute the product of the tens digits of the numbers, like so:
$$1 \times 2 = 2.$$

Adding the carry over from the tens digit, we get $2 + 1 = 3$ as the **hundreds digit**.

Then, our answer is found by putting all three results together to get
$$3 \quad 1 \quad 2 = \boxed{312}.$$

$\square$

While this process may seem a bit tricky, it will **greatly** improve the speed of your two digit multiplication.

§62.3 Squaring Tricks

In the AMC 8, we are often given problem where we have to square really large numbers. Because of the time constraint, a good trick to squaring them quickly is key. We will now talk about squaring tricks which can make squaring large numbers very simple and quick.

Problem 382

Compute: 98^2.

Proof. How would be go about this. To simplify squaring large numbers, we can use the sum and difference of squares. So how would we use the sum and difference of squares. We use it to split up a complex number into more simple and easy and to calculate numbers. So, we can split up the 98 into $100 - 2$. Now, we can use the difference of squares formula by plugging in the values of 100 and 2, in for a and b. If we do, we get the expression, $(100 - 2)^2$. If you look at this, this is still 98^2.

Now, let's expand the expression. If we use the formula that we learned when solving quadratic equations, we can expand this as $100^2 - 2 \cdot 100 \cdot 2 + 2^2$. If we simplify this, we get, $10000 - 400 + 4$. This gives us an answer of $\boxed{9604}$. $\qquad\square$

Problem 383

Compute: 34^2.

Proof. Like the last problem, we need to use the sum or difference of squares. let's find the sum or difference of two numbers which give us 34. The two numbers that we can use are 25 and 9. Now, let's substitute into the equation of sum of squares. If we substitute, we get that value, $(25 + 9)^2$ or $(25^2 + 2 \cdot 25 \cdot 9 + 9^2)$. If we simplify this, we get $625 + 450 + 81$. Simplifying this, we get that the square of 34 is, $\boxed{1156}$. $\qquad\square$

§62.4 Using Difference of Squares for Factorization

We know that

$$(a + b)(a - b) = a^2 - b^2$$

by the distributive property.

We can also go the other way like so:

$$a^2 - b^2 = (a + b)(a - b).$$

This should be no surprise to you. However, this fact can greatly help when trying to factorize a number.

Problem 384

Prime factorize

$$4187 = 66^2 - 13^2$$

given that it has two prime factors.

Proof. We know that

$$66^2 - 13^2 = (66 + 13)(66 - 13) = 79 \times 53.$$

Since we are given that the number has only two prime factors, our factors cannot be broken down more and are therefore prime numbers. Therefore, the prime factorization of 4187 is

$$\boxed{79 \times 53}.$$

□

Problem 385

Prime factorize

$$7387 = 86^2 - 3^2$$

given that there are two prime factors.

Proof. We can simplify this problem using the difference of squares factorization method:

$$86^2 - 3^2 = (86 + 3)(86 - 3) = 89 \times 83.$$

Because we are told that there are only two prime factors for the number and since we have broken down the expression into the product of two numbers, they are our prime factors. Therefore, the prime factorization of 7387 is

$$\boxed{89 \times 83}.$$

□

§63 Divisibility Rules

In the AMC 8, we often wish to prime factorize a number. When factorizing, knowing the rules of divisibility can be very helpful. We will now talk about what the most common factors we see. These factors are

$$2, 3, 4, 5, 6, 7, 8, 9, 10, 11.$$

let's talk about all of these. First, let's look at 2.

2 is a very common factor so it is very clear what we need to do to figure out if a number is divisible by it. If we are given a number and asked to figure out if it is divisible by 2, the easiest thing that we can do is just look at the units digit. If the units digit is divisible by 2, the whole number will be.

Problem 386

(Divisibility by 2)

Is the number 1248 divisible by 2? The find out what the value is if you divide 1248 by 2.

Proof. Like I said explained, we need to make sure that the units digit is divisible by 2. If we look at the units digit of 1248, we get 8. Is 8 divisible by 2? Yes it is which means that the whole number will also be divisible by 2. Now, let's find out what values we get if we divide 1248 by 2. All we have to do is simple long division. If we do, we get $\boxed{614}$. $\square$

Next, let's look at the divisibility rule of 3. Unlike 2, we use a different method to figure out if a number is divisible by 3. To do so, we need to add up all the digits of the number. If this number is divisible by 3, that means that the initial number is also divisible by 3. Now, let's look at some problems.

Problem 387

(Divisibility by 3)

IS 9636 is divisible by 3? If it is, find out what the value is if it is divisible by 3.

Proof. Using the method described, let's figure out if the number is divisible by 3. If we add up all the digits, we get 24. Since 24 is divisible by 3, that means that 9636 is also divisible by 3. Now, let's find out what we get if we divide 9363 by 3. If we do, we get that value $\boxed{3121}$. $\square$

Next, we have 4. Like 2, as long as the last two digits are divisible by 4, then the whole number will be divisible by 4. Now, let's solve some problems.

Problem 388

(Divisibility by 4)

Is 1635846924 divisible by 4? If so, find out what that value is.

Proof. Because the number is very big, the problem may look daunting, but as long as we follow that rule described, we can find if it is divisible or not. If we use the method, we need to make sure that the last two numbers are divisible by 4. If we look at it, 24 is divisible by 4, which means that 1635846924 is also divisible by 4. Now, let's find out what the value of 1635846924 divided by 4 is. If we divide it, we get that the answer is $\boxed{408961731}$. $\square$

Next, we have divisibility by 5. 5 is a very simple number to check for. This is because as long as the last number in is either 5 or 0, the number will be automatically divisible by 5. Now, using this knowledge, let's solve some problems.

Problem 389

(Divisibility by 5)

Is the number 125625 divisible by 5? If so, what is the value.

Proof. Because the rule for a number being divisible by 5 is so simple, all we have to do is just look at the number to figure out. Because the last digit is a 5, that means that the number is divisible by 5. Now, let's find out what the value of the 125625 divisible by 5. If we do, we get that the answer is $\boxed{25125}$. $\square$

Next, we have 6. Unlike all the previous numbers, we have to make sure that the number we have is divisible by 2 and 3, before we can conclude that it is divisible by 6. We already know how to make sure that the values are divisible by 2 and 3, so we just have to apply that here so that we can figure out if the number is divisible or not. Now, let's look at some problems.

Problem 390

(Divisibility by 6)

Is 1002 divisible by 6? If so, find the value.

Proof. To figure out if the number is divisible by 6, we need to make sure that the number is divisible by 2 and 3. First, let's check if the number is divisible by 2. If we look at the last digit, we see that is 2. Because 2 is divisible by 2, it means that 1002 is also divisible by 2. Next, we need to make sure that it is divisible by 3. If we add up all the digits of the number, we get 3. Because 3 is divisible by 3, it means that this number is divisible by 6. Now, let's find out what the value of 1002 divided by 6 is. If we divide, we get that the value is $\boxed{167}$. $\square$

Next, we have divisibility by 7. This one is a bit more complicated than the others, because a few more steps are required. To figure out if a number is divisible by 7, we first need to take away the last digit of the number. We then take this number and multiply it by 2. If this number subtracted from the new value is divisible by 7, that means that the whole number is divisible by 7. We then keep doing this until we get a number which is divisible by 7.

For example, if we have the number 161. If we take off the last number 1 and multiply it by 2, we get 2. We then need to subtract this value from 16 (because we took 1 off of it). If we do, we get 14, which is clearly divisible by 7. This means that the 161 is divisible by 7. Now, using this, let's solve some problems.

Problem 391

(Divisibility by 7)

Is the number 1001 divisible by 7? If so, find the value.

Proof. To start off, we need to take off the last digit of the number and multiply it by 2. If we do, we get $1 \cdot 2$, giving us 2. We then subtract this from 100. If we do, we get the value, 98. Because 98 is divisible by 7, 1001 is also divisible by 7. Now, let's find out what that value is. If we divide 1001 by 7, we get, $\boxed{143}$. □

Next, we have 9. Just like 3, if the sum of the digits is divisible by 9, that means that it is also divisible 9. We can also iterate this process over and over again until you know for sure that the number is divisible by 9. Now, let's solve some problems.

Problem 392

(Divisibility by 9)

Is 1008 divisible by 9? If so, find the its value.

Proof. If we want to make sure that the number is divisible by 9, we need to check if the sum of the digits are divisible. If we add all the digits, we get 9. Since 9 is divisible by 9, that means that 1008 is also divisible by 9. Now, we need to find what the value of 1008 divided by 9 is. If we divide, we get that it is, $\boxed{112}$. □

Next, we have divisibility by 10. 10 is by far one of the most simplest to check for because all we have to do is make sure that the last digit of the number is 0. If it is, it will automatically be divisible by 10. Now, let's solve some problems related to this.

Problem 393

(Divisibility by 10)

Is 45260 divisible by 10? If so, what is the value.

Proof. To prove that the number is divisible by 10, all we have to do is check the last digit. In the number 45260, the last digit is 0, which means that the number is divisible by 10. Now, let's find out what the value of 45260 divided by 10. If we solve, we get that that value is $\boxed{4526}$. □

Finally, we divisibility by 11. This one, like divisibility by 7, is uncommon and a bit more complex than the other ones. To check if a number is divisible by 11, we have to first take each digit of the number. We then add up every alternating digit. Once we have the sums of alternating digits, we subtract them. If this number is divisible by 11, then that means that the original number is divisible by 11.

For example, If we have the number 9999, we have to take the alternating digits. In this case, the sum of the alternating digits is 18 and 18, because we have $9 + 9$ and $9 + 9$. Now, we have to subtract the sum of these. If we do, we get 0, because $18 - 18$ is 0. Since 0 is divisible by 11, that means that 9999 is also divisible by 11.

Problem 394

(Divisibility by 11)

Is the number 1234567895 divisible by 11? If so, what is the value.

Proof. To confirm whether or not the number is divisible by 11 or not, we need to add up the alternating digits. In this case, the first sum of alternating digits would be

$$1 + 3 + 5 + 7 + 9,$$

which gives us 25. The next sum would be

$$2 + 4 + 6 + 8 + 5,$$

which gives us 25. Now, if we subtract the two, we get 0. Because 0 is divisible by 11, that means that 1234567895 is also divisible by 11. Now, let's find the value of 1234567895 divided by 11. If we do, we get $\boxed{112233445}$. □

Made in the USA
Las Vegas, NV
09 November 2022

59048613R00145